92785

F/F #16

Dragonflies
of Surrey

Dragonflies
of Surrey

PETER FOLLETT

PRINCIPAL RECORDERS
DAVID BALDOCK
DAVID AND JEAN DELL
ROGER HAWKINS
MIKE THURNER

SURREY WILDLIFE TRUST

Cover illustration: Brilliant Emerald Dragonfly, by David Element

ISBN 0 9526065 1 8

British Library Cataloguing-in-Publication Data.
A catalogue record for this book is available
from the British Library.

First published 1996
by Surrey Wildlife Trust
School Lane, Pirbright, Woking, Surrey GU24 0JN.

FOREWORD

With this book Surrey joins the counties which have their own regional dragonfly volume.

Not before time, as the county includes some of our finest dragonfly areas and, with 28 breeding species, comes just one species behind neighbouring Sussex and Hampshire which are the richest in the country. To do justice to this fauna, many thousands of individual records have gone into compiling this guide and the author has spent hundreds of hours collating and checking them to make it as comprehensive as possible. It is now over 40 years since I began dragonfly watching in Surrey. Looking back to my earliest days, it is encouraging to be able to record that all the species I knew then are still with us in the county and two, perhaps three, considered rare then are actually known to be more frequent now.

To get a longer perspective, W.J.Lucas published his *British Dragonflies* at the very beginning of the century and at that time knew only 26 breeding species in the county. Since then we have added White-faced Darter and Brillant Emerald which were totally unknown in the South of England in 1900. The former only holds on tenuously to one site today but the latter is now known to be quite common in suitable areas and is probably still extending its range. Two more species, Golden-ringed Dragonfly and Ruddy Darter, known from just one site each in 1900, are much more widely recorded today. The Golden-ringed Dragonfly must surely have been overlooked and its distribution today is probably not very different from what it was then, but the Ruddy Darter has undoubtedly expanded its range and is now widely spread through the county.

So is it all good news? Obviously not. I am sure most of us know dragonfly sites that have deteriorated or even disappeared in recent years. Fouling up and even well-meaning but injudicious clearing up of ponds, canalisation and over-zealous clearing of streams and ditches can all have disastrous results for aquatic life. In the long term, the pressure for more and more water extraction for domestic use is probably the greatest threat. Gradual erosion of the water table may be hardly noticed much of the time, but combine this with a year of drought just a little more severe than we have seen in some recent years and disaster could come quite rapidly to some species.

Surrey is a crowded county with heavy pressures on much of its countryside and it is remarkable that an aquatic group like the dragonflies have survived as long as they have. The future is going to pose problems and threats to their continued existence It is here that anyone with a little knowledge and sufficient interest can play a part by visiting local areas and monitoring the health or otherwise of habitats and if necessary giving early warning of any problems that may be developing. If an increasing number of enthusiasts do this, as they have done in recent years, perhaps at the end of the 21st century someone will be able to write that Surrey still hasn't lost a breeding species.

DON TAGG

The Environment Agency has legal duties to further conservation when carrying out its functions and to promote the conservation of flora and fauna dependent on the aquatic environment. The Agency, therefore, devotes significant resources to creating and enhancing watercourses and wetland habitats for the benefit of a wide range of wildlife, including dragonflies. We are, therefore, delighted to help with the promotion of local knowledge about dragonflies and their habitats through our collaborative funding of this splendid book.

ALASTAIR DRIVER
Conservation Manager
Environment Agency (Thames Region)

CONTENTS

PREFACE

Surrey is a county of contrasts, from the acid heathlands and their associated bogs in the west to the ridges of chalk in the north-east, and with the sandstone in the south grading to low meadowland in the east. These areas are crossed by rivers and canals, such as the Wey, Mole, Tillingbourne and Basingstoke Canal, which are mixed together with an abundance of lakes and ponds to form a mosaic of habitats highly suited to the rich assemblage of dragonfly species found in the county, some of which are of national importance.

Due to its close proximity to London, and the ever increasing threats to the countryside, especially to the remaining tracts of lowland heaths, we should be ever watchful and vigilant in safeguarding such an area for the long-term future, not only of dragonflies but of all the wildlife that occurs in the county.

I hope that this atlas will form a baseline for future recording and give an idea of the distribution, abundance and diversity of the dragonfly fauna in Surrey.

ACKNOWLEDGEMENTS

I would like to thank all the members of the Hampshire and Surrey Borders group of the British Dragonfly Society for their records and survey work, mainly from the west of the county and especially from the Basingstoke Canal and Thursley National Nature Reserve. My thanks also go to Stephen Brooks, the recorder for the London Natural History Society, for supplying all the dragonfly records pertaining to Surrey from his files, and to Alan Hold and Noelle Welstead, the Odonata Recording Scheme regional recorders for south-east England, for all the Surrey records from their files.

Special thanks must go to David Baldock for supplying his survey data from 1970-1980 which forms the backbone of this atlas, together with numerous references and much historical data, for which I am deeply indebted, and to Roger Hawkins who has sent records consistently, first to David Baldock and later to me, mainly from the south-east of the county. I also thank David and Jean Dell for their consistent and detailed recording, especially from the western heaths and Basingstoke Canal; they have set an example to us all in Surrey.

I owe a very special thank you to Mike Thurner for his help and guidance in the use of the Recorder computer database and assistance with the production of this atlas in so many other ways. My thanks also go to Don Tagg for his advice, guidance and knowledge, and for writing the foreword to this book; to Jill Silsby for refereeing and Roger Hawkins for proofreading; to Edmund Jarzembowski and André Nel for writing the geological and fossil history; to Martin Newman and staff (Surrey Wildlife Trust) for securing the required finance and supporting the Surrey Invertebrate Atlas Project; to Clare Windsor for guiding me through the jungle of production and publishing, and for handling the book's design; to John Pontin for his advice and guidance on conservation matters and his critical appraisal of the various drafts of this book; to David Element, Mike Thurner and others for donating their magnificent photographs; and to Messrs P. Crabb and H. Taylor for supplying Plate 2, figures 4 and 6 respectively.

Many other naturalists have supplied records that have contributed to the depth of coverage shown on the maps – their names are listed opposite; to all of them I offer my most sincere thanks.

Finally, I am indebted to the Environment Agency and to English Nature, without whose financial contributions this book would not exist.

LIST OF RECORDERS

Abbott S.
Adams P.A.
Alexander K.N.A.
Allen C.A.
Allen P.M.
Andrews J.
Annett H.E.
Arnott P.A.
Arnott J.G.L.
Ashby C.B.
Ashdown W.J.
Atkins N.
Attlee H.G.
Attridge W.
Averill M.
Bailey S.
Baker R.
Baldock D.W.
Beuk P.
Beven G.
Bickford P.
Birchall M.J.
Bishop E.B.
Booth F.
Boyle M.
Bratton J.H.
Brocklesby J.S.
Brook J.F.
Brook G.G.
Brooks S.
Brough P.
Bunce M.
Charles P.J.
Clarke K.
Classey E.W.
Coleman D.A.
Collins G.A.
Cowley J.
Dawson D.G.
Day R.
Dell C.
Dell D.H.
Dell J.
Dempsey M.J.
Dimmock D.P.

Dobson J.
Donnithorne N.J.
Early J.P.
Element D.
Emmett V.E.
Emmett E.E.
Enfield M.A.
Follett P.C.
Follett S.A.
Fraser D.
Frith M.
Fry R.M.
Gittings T.
Gray A.S.
Greenaway F.
Guy S.M.
Hall C.R.
Hallam N.
Hallam R.
Hastings R.B.
Havers J.R.
Hawkins R.D.
Herlihy D.
Higgs A.B.
Hill R.
Johnson K.
Kett S.M.
Kettle R.
Kirk R.S.
Lowmass C.D.
Lynes M.
Malton N.
Matthews M.G.
Merritt R.
Miller P.L.
Morris R.K.A.
Mundell A.R.G.
Murdoch D.A.
Nelson B.
Norriss T.N.
Oates J.
Orton R.
Parker J.I.
Parkinson A.
Petrie A.B.

Phillips N.J.
Phillips V.E.
Pontin J.
Price S.O.V.
Redford S.
Reed W.
Reed A.
Reynolds F.L.
Richards A.W.
Riley J.A.
Robinson G.
Sage M.
Sampson R.D.
Sankey J.
Scott A.N.
Silsby J.D.
Simpson P.J.
Steer J.B.
Stenning J.
Summersby L.
Sussex D.J.
Tagg D.
Tarbat J.E.
Telfer M.G.
Thompson R.
Thurner M.R.L.
Vick G.S.
Vickers J.G.
Vincent E.
Wain C.B.
Wain W.H.
Walker F.A.
Ward-Smith J.
Whitaker W.
Winsland D.
Young P.A.

SURREY – THE VICE-COUNTY

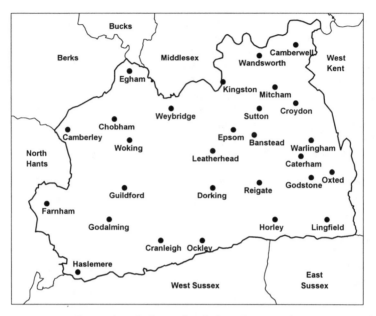

Surrey in relation to bordering vice-counties

For any biological recording, it is essential to have a stable boundary unaffected by the continuing boundary changes of the politicians. Such a system exists in the form of the vice-county, a division originally proposed by H.C.Watson in 1852 in order to provide a set of unit areas of roughly similar dimensions for botanical recording. This system was adopted by many zoologists in the succeeding years and is now the accepted form for the recording of biological data. The vice-county system is explained in text and maps in Dandy (1969).

The vice-county of Surrey (VC17) differs from the current administrative county principally in its northern boundary which is marked by the course of the River Thames, thus including the boroughs of the south-western quadrant of Greater London. The southern boundary differs slightly in that it runs almost east-west in the vicinity of Horley and so includes the area occupied by Gatwick Airport which is currently in West Sussex, and on the western boundary an area of approximately one square kilometre to the south of the village of Batt's Corner, and part of present day Surrey, is excluded. The other major exclusion is the district of Spelthorne, which only became attached to Surrey in 1965, and in fact belongs principally to the vice-county of Middlesex (VC21).

GEOLOGY AND FOSSIL RECORD

by Edmund Jarzembowski and André Nel

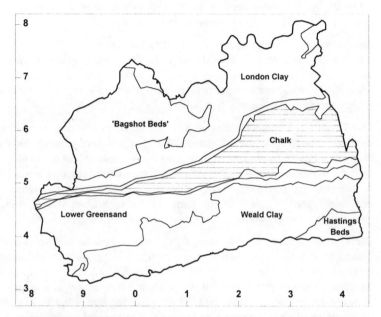

Figure 1. Solid geology of Surrey, after 'Butterflies of Surrey'.

Geologically speaking, the county of Surrey occupies part of the eroded northern limb of the Wealden anticline (anticlinorium) and corresponding Thames Valley syncline, both formed in the late Tertiary (Miocene) during the Alpine Orogeny. This means that the rocks strike approximately East-West with the oldest in the South and the youngest in the North (Figure 1).

The strata are all of sedimentary origin and range in age from Early Cretaceous in the Weald to Eocene in the Thames Valley. This solid geology is covered (especially in valleys) by various superficial deposits dating from the Pleistocene and even post-glacial times. The highest ground is found on the more competent rocks in the south, notably the chalk and greensand ridges, the latter providing the highest point in South-East England at Leith Hill.

Unlike other parts of the geological system, the Wealden Supergroup ('Beds' of earlier authors) is essentially non-marine and famous for finds of dinosaur bones and other terrestrial organisms. More recently, the Wealden has yielded an interesting Odonata fauna adding to our knowledge of Early Cretaceous aquatic life. The insect remains occur in the Weald Clay which spans two stages (Hauterivian and Barremian) some 125-135 million years Before Present (Harland *et al.*, 1990). The fossils have been described from brickworks at Clockhouse (TQ 175385), Auclaye (170388) and Smokejacks (115372), but have also been found in other pits such as at Beare Green (South Holmwood, 185421) and Newdigate (205425).

Fossil Odonata are represented mainly by detached wings and body segments preserved in siltstone (e.g. Clockhouse), clay ironstone (e.g. Smokejacks) and phosphatic concretions (e.g. Auclaye). Not all the fossils are disarticulated (Plate 1, figure 1) and one particularly well-preserved specimen has been dubbed the Surrey Dragonfly (see below).

The Weald Clay palaeoenvironment is envisaged as a warm, low-lying wetland prone to some salination and the dragonflies were probably blown in or carried down by streams from the now eroded upland (Londinia) to the north (Jarzembowski, 1995). The Odonata fauna includes representatives of all three living suborders: Anisoptera (dragonflies), Zygoptera (damselflies) and Anisozygoptera , the latter now found relict outside Europe. In addition, there is a late representative of the extinct suborder Archizygoptera.

The fossils are being actively studied: 15 species have been described or figured to date and more new taxa are currently in preparation including representatives of the extinct family Aeschnidiidae and extant family Gomphidae of earlier authors. All this work is based on adults and larval remains are yet to be described. More material is needed to clarify relationships of already recognised species and to help establish new ones.

This is PRIS contribution no. 498 for EJ.

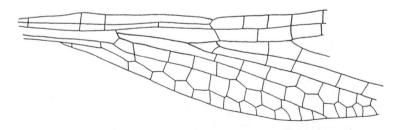

Figure 2. Species A, wing after Bechly et al., (1997 in press). Coenagrionoid/hemiphlebioid, CH. Length 9 mm.

FOSSIL CHECKLIST

TAXONOMIC DISCLAIMER: in view of the fact that some of the species herein have not been published formally at time of writing, this publication is not deemed to be valid for taxonomic purposes [under ICZN Article 8b].

Brickworks' abbreviations: A – Auclaye CH – Clockhouse S – Smokejacks † denotes extinct family.

SUBORDER ZYGOPTERA

Family Coenagrionidae Kirby, 1890
Mesocoenagrion martinae Bechly, Martínez-Delclòs, Jarzembowski, Nel, Escuillé & Coram, 1997 in press (Plate 1, figure 3) A.
Comment: this is an early record of this living family.

† Family Cretacoenagrionidae Bechly, 1994
Comment: a systematically difficult family with only one included species:
Cretacoenagrion alleni Jarzembowski, 1990 (Plate 1, figure 2) CH.

Family Uncertain
Cretarchistigma greenwoodi Bechly *et al.*, 1997 in press (Plate 2, figure 4) A, CH.
Species A Bechly *et al.*, 1997 in press (Figure 2) CH.

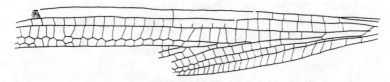

***Figure 3.** Protomyrmeleon cretacicus, CH, wing after Nel and Jarzembowski (Under review). Length 23 mm.*

†SUBORDER ARCHIZYGOPTERA

†Family Protomyrmeleontidae Handlirsch, 1906
Protomyrmeleon cretacicus t. s. name Nel & Jarzembowski (Figure 3) CH.
Comment: this is a late record of this extinct Mesozoic family and archaic suborder.

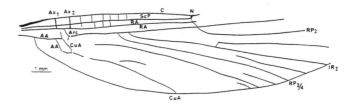

Figure 4. Campterophlebiid? hindwing, CH,
after Nel & Jarzembowski (1996).

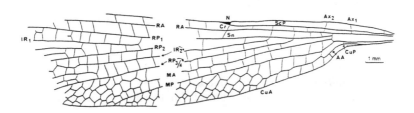

Figure 5. Mesoepiophlebia bexleyae, CH, hindwing
after Nel & Jarzembowski (1996).

SUBORDER 'ANISOZYGOPTERA'

†Family Campterophlebiidae Handlirsch, 1908
Doubtful unnamed species (Figure 4) CH.

Family Epiophlebiidae Tillyard, 1921
Comment: living family represented by one extant genus found in the Himalayas and Japan.
Mesoepiophlebia bexleyae Nel & Jarzembowski, 1996 (Figure 5) CH.

†Family Euthemistidae Pritykina, 1968
Comment: extinct family typically known from the Upper Jurassic of Kazakhstan and distinguished by a line of veins across the wing base (indicated by arrow in Figure 6).
†*Proeuthemis pritykinae* Nel & Jarzembowski, 1996 (Figure 6) CH.

†Family Tarsophlebiidae Handlirsch, 1906
Comment: extinct family typically known from the Upper Jurassic Solnhofen Limestone of Bavaria.
Tarsophlebia sp. Jarzembowski, 1990 (Plate 2, figure 5) CH.

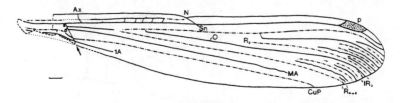

Figure 6. Proeuthemis pritykinae, *CH, forewing after Jarzembowski (1990). Scale line = 1 mm.*

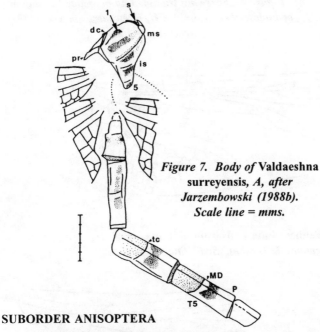

Figure 7. Body of Valdaeshna surreyensis, *A, after Jarzembowski (1988b). Scale line = mms.*

SUBORDER ANISOPTERA

†Family Aeschnidiidae Handlirsch, 1906

Comment: distinctive large wings with dense wing venation, elongate triangles and frequent dark colouration in Wealden.

Undescribed species A, S, CH.

Family Aeshnidae Leach, 1815/†Family Cymatophlebiidae Handlirsch, 1906

Comment: the named species is the Surrey Dragonfly and the best preserved Cretaceous odonatan found so far in southern England:

Valdaeshna surreyensis Jarzembowski, 1988b (Plate 3, figure 7; Figure 7) A.

Unnamed species (Plate 3, figure 8; Figure 8) CH.

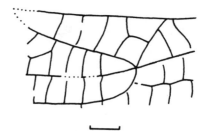

Figure 8. Forewing triangle and associated venation of undescribed aeshnid, CH, after Jarzembowski (1987). Scale line = 1 mm.

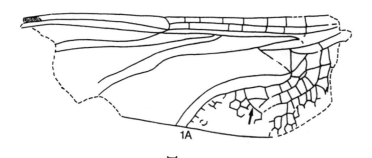

Figure 9. Valdicordulia wellsorum, *CH, hindwing after Jarzembowski (1988a). Scale line = 1 mm.*

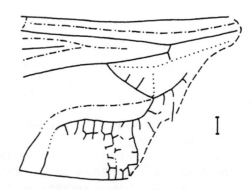

Figure 10. Hindwing base of gomphid (auct.), CH, after Jarzembowski (1987). Scale line = 1 mm.

Family Corduliidae Selys-Longchamps, 1850
Cretaneophya strevensi Jarzembowski & Nel, 1996
(Plate 3, figure 9) A, CH, S.
Valdicordulia wellsorum Jarzembowski & Nel, 1996
(Figure 9) CH.
Comment: *Cretaneophya* has a near relative *Araripelibellula* from the upper Lower Cretaceous of Brazil (Aptian stage: coeval with the Lower Greensand of the UK). *Cretaneophya* must be the smallest Surrey dragonfly belonging to a group with a wingspan of only 35 mm. *Valdicordulia* has a distinctly elongate anal loop (indicated by an arrow in Figure 9). Libelluloids are generally uncommon in the Mesozoic.

Family Gomphidae Rambur, 1842
Undescribed species (Plate 2, figure 6; Figure 10) A, CH.

(References – see page 67.)

HISTORY OF SURREY RECORDING

Dragonfly recording in Surrey began in the nineteenth century with W.E.Leach who, in 'Brewsters Edinborough Encyclopedia' (1815), mentions *Orthetrum cancellatum* as being common on the Croydon Canal. The next publication of interest, Stephens' 'Entomology Mandibulata' Vol.vi (1835), gives numerous references to Surrey species such as *Platycnemis pennipes*, plentiful in July at Walsham Meadows near Ripley (where it still occurs abundantly today), *Anax imperator* on Wimbledon Common, *Aeshna mixta* uncommonly at Godalming and Ripley, *Cordulegaster boltonii* and *Cordulia aenea* also at Godalming, along with *Libellula quadrimaculata* and *Orthetrum coerulescens*. In 1845 W.F.Evans, in his book 'British Libellulinae', gives *Ceriagrion tenellum* from Weybridge, *Platycnemis pennipes*, again from Ripley, and *Libellula quadrimaculata* f. *praenubila* from Godalming.

Recording obviously continued and in 1890 W.Harcourt Bath published his 'Illustrated Handbook of British Dragonflies' wherein he mentions *Lestes sponsa* from Ripley, *Platycnemis pennipes* again from Walsham Meadows, *Aeshna mixta* from Ripley, Godalming and Norwood as "being rare but widely distributed", *Libellula quadrimaculata* including f. *praenubila*, *Orthetrum coerulescens* and abundant *Cordulia aenea*, all from Godalming, with *Orthetrum cancellatum* still abundant on the Croydon Canal.

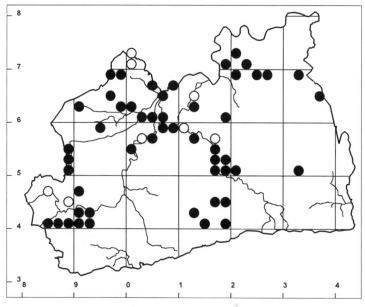

Total records to 1969

The publication by W.J.Lucas of 'British Dragonflies' in 1900 probably did more to increase interest in and knowledge of this group than any other publication of this period, and it is still today one of the finest books on the British dragonflies ever produced. There are numerous records from Surrey in this book, probably due to the fact that Lucas lived all his life in Byfleet and Kingston-upon-Thames and collected assiduously in the county, using many of the specimens caught in Surrey, adults, larvae and exuviae, to illustrate both this book and his further publication 'The Aquatic (Naiad) Stage of the British Dragonflies' (1930). Among the most interesting records are *Sympetrum vulgatum*, a male taken at Bookham Common by C.A.Briggs in 1891, *Sympetrum fonscolombii* at Ockham Common on 8th and 17th June 1892, all males, again by C.A.Briggs, *Sympetrum flaveolum* at Ockham Common and Elstead during September 1898 and again in 1899. *Sympetrum sanguineum* is mentioned as occurring in only one locality in the county, Ockham Common, but today it occurs in over fifty.

Two interesting species not recorded in Surrey up to this time, *Leucorrhinia dubia* and *Somatochlora metallica*, were both considered northern species until the discovery of the former on Thursley Common in 1933 and of the latter in 1939 by A.W.Richards, again at Thursley. One other species of special interest from this period, *Ischnura pumilio*, was recorded from a boggy runnel in Richmond Park by H.G.Attlee in 1931 but only survived there until 1933.

Recording and study continued in the county with work by C.Longfield, described in her book 'The Dragonflies of the British Isles', and by C.O.Hammond, a resident of Surrey, who wrote many articles and notes in the entomological journals of the day, and who in 1977 published an identification guide that was to encourage many people to take up the study of dragonflies. Another resident of the county, A.E.Gardner, had undertaken the work of describing the early stages of the majority of British species, using examples obtained in Surrey, as the basis of many articles in the 'Entomologist's Gazette' and 'The Entomologist', culminating in an illustrated key to the aquatic larval stages that was repeated in Hammond's book.

The period from 1970 to 1980 is notable for the first attempt at a complete survey of the county, undertaken by D.W.Baldock. This produced a series of maps giving a much better idea of the distribution of not only the rarer species, but all those known to occur in Surrey at that time. He was ably supported in this task by R.D.Hawkins who was responsible for the majority of records from the south-east of the county, these greatly extending the range of such species as *Somatochlora metallica*, *Cordulia aenea* and *Platycnemis pennipes*.

The formation of the British Dragonfly Society in 1983 led to the setting up of local groups, and in 1989 a Surrey group was started by J.Arnott, A.Mundell

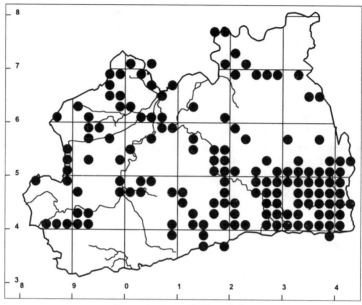

Records from 1970 to 1980

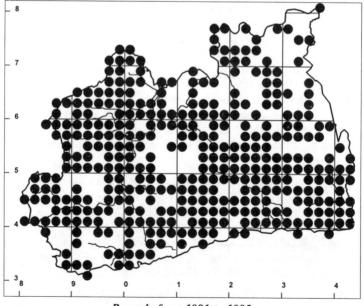

Records from 1981 to 1995

and D.Tagg along with other interested people, all concerned with the protection and study of dragonflies. This led to a more consistent recording effort, with M.Thurner acting as co-ordinator for the accumulation of records on a computer database to produce a series of maps detailing the records received and the future recording requirements. Many separate studies were started, namely, the group's contribution to the B.R.C. Key Sites Project, continuous and detailed work on the Basingstoke Canal, and surveys of Thursley Common, Normandy Pond, Thundry Meadows Reserve, Henleypark Lake and the Blackwater Valley.

The amount of data collected led in 1992 to the author's involvement with the processing and collating of records, due to M.Thurner's other commitments. It was also suggested that once all the records were on the Recorder database, a series of maps could be distributed to all the recorders who supplied data and to other sources who might provide additional records. This was achieved and sets of provisional maps were distributed in April 1994 and again in September 1994, which led to a more consistent coverage throughout the county. During late 1993, Surrey Wildlife Trust formed a small group of natural history recorders to look at the feasibility of producing a series of atlases on invertebrates. This atlas project started with 'Butterflies of Surrey' in 1995, and is followed by this volume as the second in a series of publications to be produced annually over the next few years.

FUTURE RECORDING

It is important that recording continues in the county after publication of this atlas, in order to monitor any changes in species' distribution, breeding habitats and ecological requirements, and to safeguard sites and the species which they contain.

Any further records, especially with proof of breeding, or site surveys, will be welcomed either by the author or by Surrey Wildlife Trust and will in due course be forwarded to the regional Odonata recorders, to be added to the national database.

DRAGONFLY HABITATS

Lakes, Ponds, Clay, Gravel and Chalk Pits, Reservoirs

Surrey is a county which includes all of the above habitat types, of which some occur in greater numbers than others, but all are important to the breeding and feeding requirements of their dragonfly inhabitants.

Waterside vegetation, such as willows, alders, nettles and long grass, offering good shelter, feeding and roosting areas, is important, together with good emergent vegetation, especially water lilies, water plantain (*Alisma plantago-aquatica*), soft rush (*Juncus effusus*), broad-leaved pondweed (*Potamogeton natans*) and great reedmace (*Typha latifolia*). Unfortunately many ponds and pits have been neglected over the years, either being allowed to fill with vegetation and dry out, or being used as sites for rubbish disposal. Over-stocking and over-fishing have also led to the degradation of some lakes, often with severe erosion of the banks and damage to emergent plants.

Recently there has been a growing emphasis by local councils, sympathetic landowners and other interested parties to clear out and restore many of these sites and to appreciate not only their potential for wildlife but also their amenity and aesthetic value to the local communities. Some of the more notable sites in this category include Hedgecourt Lake, Bay Pond (both Surrey Wildlife Trust reserves), Bolder Mere, Newdigate Brickworks, Earlswood Lakes, Vachery Pond, Frensham Little and Great Ponds, and Langhams Pond at Runnymede.

For typical species found in these habitats see Table 1 opposite, but because of the number of waters of this type in the county, only a selection can be given to illustrate species diversity. (See Plate 4.)

Table 1 – Ponds and Lakes

> B = Breeding at site
> + = Occurring at site

Site	MapRef	*L. sponsa*	*P. nymphula*	*E. najas*	*C. puella*	*E. cyathigerum*	*A. mixta*	*A. cyanea*	*A. grandis*	*A. imperator*	*C. aenea*	*L. quadrimaculata*	*L. depressa*	*O. cancellatum*	*S. striolatum*	*S. sanguineum*
Albury Mill Ponds	TQ0448		B	B	B	B	+		B						B	B
Bay Pond, Godstone	TQ3551	B	B	+	B	B	+	B		B	B		B		B	B
Black Pond, Esher	TQ1262	B	B	B	B	B	+	B	B	B	B	B	B	+	B	B
Bolder Mere, Wisley	TQ0758	B	B	+	B	B	B	B	B	B	B	B	B	B	B	B
Bookham Common Ponds	TQ1356	B	B		B	B	+	B	B	B	B	B	B	B	B	B
Brook Pond, Whitmoor	SU9853	B	B	B	B	B		B	B	B	B	B	B	B	B	B
Bury Hill Lake, Westcott	TQ1547		B	B	B	B		+		B	B		B		B	+
Duncan Fraser Reserve, Capel	TQ1740	B	B		B	B	B	B	B	B		B	B	B	B	B
Earlswood Lakes	TQ2648	B	+	B	B	B			B	B	+				B	B
Frensham Little Pond	SU8641	B	+	B	B	B	+	B	B	B		B			B	B
Frensham Great Pond	SU8440			B	B	B	+		+	B					B	B
Hedgecourt Lake, Felbridge	TQ3540	B	B	B	B	B	B	B	B	B	B	B	B	B	B	B
Langhams Pond, Runnymede	TQ0071	B	B	B	B	B	+	B	B	B	B	B	B	+	B	B
Normandy Pond	SU9251	B	B	B	B	B	+	B	B	B	B	B	B	B	B	B
Old Newdigate Brickworks	TQ2042	B	B	B	B	B	+	B	B	B	B	B	B	B	B	B
Vann Lake, Ockley	TQ1539	B	B	B	B	B	+	B	B	B	B	B	B	B	B	

Rivers, Streams and Canals

On looking at the map of Surrey it is clear that the county is well-endowed with this type of habitat, ranging from wide slow-flowing rivers, such as the Mole and the Eden, to the Wey, which is slow-flowing in parts but with gravel-bottomed faster-flowing stretches on its more southerly reaches. Much of the northern part of the River Wey has been canalised, creating an interesting range of habitats with slow backwaters and fast-flowing parts where the river flows over weirs, rejoining the canal sections further downstream. One of the best examples of this habitat type must be the nationally important Basingstoke Canal, with its rich assemblage of species, which for most of its length has been designated a Site of Special Scientific Interest.

In recent years the quality of the river water has undergone a considerable improvement, due to the efforts of conservation bodies and the National Rivers Authority. This has resulted in an increase in species abundance and diversity to levels not seen on some rivers for some time. One of the species to gain from improved quality of habitat is *Platycnemis pennipes* (White-legged Damselfly), especially on the River Eden where it occurs in enormous numbers, and on the River Mole where it has recolonised stretches on which it had not been seen for many years. This is a particularly good species for use in monitoring river quality, since it appears to be very susceptible to water pollution and poor riverside habitat, so it is often used as an indicator species. A further species, *Cordulegaster boltonii* (Golden-ringed Dragonfly), has also apparently increased in recent years, especially on the small streams issuing from the sandstone ridge running from Leith Hill westwards. These streams, such as the Tillingbourne, are extremely clean and hold a good species diversity, especially where they reach the flatter meadowlands.

The principal rivers and canals, together with associated species, are listed opposite in Table 2. (See Plate 5.)

Table 2 – Rivers, Streams and Canals

B = Breeding at site
+ = Occurring at site

Site	*C. virgo*	*C. splendens*	*P. pennipes*	*C. puella*	*A. mixta*	*A. cyanea*	*A. grandis*	*B. pratense*	*C. boltonii*	*C. aenea*	*S. metallica*
Basingstoke Canal	+	B	+	B	B	B	B	B	+	B	B
Eden Brook	+	B	B	B	+	B	B			+	+
North River	B	B		B	+	+	+				
River Eden	+	B	B	B	+	B	B				+
River Mole	B	B	B	B	+	B	B				
River Thames		+		B	+	+	+				
River Wey North	+	B	B	B	B	B	B			+	
River Wey South	B	B	B	B	+	B	B			B	+
Thursley Stream	+	B		B	+	B	+	+	B		+
Tillingbourne	+	B	B	B	+	B	B			B	B
Wey & Arun Junction Canal		+		B	+	B	B			+	

Heaths, Bogs and associated Acidic Ponds and Lakes

This habitat occurs mainly in the west of the county, where some of the best lowland heaths remaining in Britain are found. They are also the richest in terms of dragonfly species, many of which prefer acidic conditions in which to breed. It is therefore naturally in the western half of the county that most occur, sometimes in enormous numbers. Chobham Common and Thursley Common, both National Nature Reserves, are the best examples of this type of habitat in Surrey.

Other excellent sites include some of the vast tracts of heathland used by the armed forces, areas such as the Pirbright and Bisley Ranges together with Colony Bog, Westend Common, the Surrey Wildlife Trust reserve on Brentmoor Heath and Henleypark Lake, with its surrounding heathland to the south of Pirbright. That Surrey Wildlife Trust has a further three reserves of this habitat type – Wentworth, Bagmoor Common and Gracious Pond – testifies to its importance, especially as the rate of disappearance of heathland in Surrey is over 90% in the last 200 years, and in the region of 16% in the last 10 years.

Typical species of lowland heath include the very rare *Leucorrhinia dubia* (White-faced Darter), with only one locality in Surrey at Thursley Common, *Ceriagrion tenellum* (Small Red Damselfly), *Orthetrum coerulescens* (Keeled Skimmer), *Aeshna juncea* (Common Hawker) and *Sympetrum danae* (Black Darter).

Table 3 opposite lists the better sites, together with their associated species, but it must be stressed that not all are open to the public. (See Plate 6.)

Table 3 – Heathland and Bogs

B = Breeding at site
+ = Occurring at site
(+) = Old record

Site	Map Ref	E. najas	C. tenellum	A. juncea	A. imperator	B. pratense	C. boltonii	C. aenea	S. metallica	L. quadrimaculata	O. coerulescens	S. danae	L. dubia
Brentmoor Heath, West End	SU9360	+		B									
Broomhall Heath, Wentworth	SU9666		B	+	B					B		B	
Chobham Common NNR	SU9765	B	B	B	B	B	B	B	+	B	+	B	
Esher Pond	TQ1362	B	B	B	B	B	B	B	B	B		B	
Gracious Pond, Chobham	SU9864	B	B	+	+			B	+			+	
Henleypark Lake	SU9353	B	B	B	B		B	B	B	B	B	B	
Lightwater Country Park	SU9162	B			B			B		B	B	B	
Royal Common, Elstead	SU9242	B		B	B		B	B		B	B	B	
Thursley NNR	SU9041	B	B	B	B	B	B	B	B	B	B	B	B
Westend Common, Pirbright Ranges	SU9260		B		+		+			B	+	+	
Whitmoor Common	SU9853	B		B	B			B		+	B	+	B
Wisley Common	TQ0759	B	B	B	B	+		B		B		B	(+)

CONSERVATION

It is easy when considering dragonflies to concentrate on the rarer species and their conservation priorities, and to neglect the more widespread species. When taken in a wider context, it is the total number of species found at a particular site that gives a better picture and indication of the suitability and quality of the habitat.

The criteria for a good dragonfly site consist of: a habitat that is relatively undisturbed and plentifully supplied with aquatic, emergent and some waterside vegetation affording shelter; good adjacent hunting and feeding territories; and clean water for their aquatic larvae to flourish. These conditions are not always easy to attain, since it is often a matter of balancing nature and habitat conservation against leisure interests such as water sports, boating and fishing, together with the needs of industry.

The main threats to dragonfly habitat in Surrey are the drainage of small ponds and pits, often in conjunction with land reclamation schemes and infilling with rubbish, the chemical pollution of waterways by industry, and agricultural runoff, especially in the more intensively farmed south-east of the county, together with the clearing of banks and canalisation of streams and rivers. Heathlands and bogs may on the one hand be destroyed by drainage or ploughing up for agricultural use, or on the other be allowed to deteriorate through the lack of grazing or other appropriate management, since some control of invasive plant-life is required to stem the natural succession to scrub or woodland. The continued high level of fishing activities within the county has been both a boon and a curse, with the preservation of good clean wetland habitat often offset by overstocking, the destruction of reedswamp areas, and bank erosion. The much publicised 'global warming' may also create its own problems, with the drying up of wetlands and an increase in algal blooms, as has occurred recently at Frensham Great Pond. Last but by no means least is the threat to the canals, due to the ever increasing demand for boating, especially on the Basingstoke Canal with its rich flora and fauna. This brings with it pollution in the form of rubbish and oil film, together with the destruction of canal-side and floating vegetation, and increased turbidity.

The safeguarding of these wetland habitats can be a difficult exercise, as shown in the restoration of the Great Pond on Epsom Common, and the Basingstoke Canal. Bringing threatened sites to the notice of public authorities, conservation bodies and owners, together with providing accurate biological data and recommendations for management, all help in preserving such sites and the flora and fauna they contain. Dragonflies are good indicators of site quality and it is notable that any such site in Surrey with seventeen or more species qualifies for consideration as a Site of Special Scientific Interest (see Appendix 1). That the overall status of dragonflies in the county is very good, is due to the vigilance of all those concerned with their study and protection, which has increased greatly over the last decade. This has enabled such sites as Henleypark Lake, Black Pond at Esher, Normandy Pond, Thursley Common and the Basingstoke Canal, together with the Surrey Wildlife Trust reserves of Thundry Meadows, Bay Pond and Hedgecourt Lake, to remain excellent sites for the study of dragonflies.

CHECKLIST OF SURREY DRAGONFLIES

KEY

B	Breeding in Surrey
Eb	Formerly bred, now extinct in Surrey
Mb	Migrant that has bred in Surrey
RV	Rare vagrant
M	Migrant
R	Rare visitor from adjacent counties, not thought to breed in Surrey
[*]	Doubtful record

ORDER ODONATA

SUBORDER Zygoptera

Calopterygidae

Calopteryx virgo (Linnaeus, 1758)	Beautiful Demoiselle	B
Calopteryx splendens (Harris, 1782)	Banded Demoiselle	B

Lestidae

Lestes sponsa (Hansemann, 1823)	Emerald Damselfly	B
Lestes dryas Kirby, 1890	Scarce Emerald Damselfly	RV

Platycnemididae

Platycnemis pennipes (Pallas, 1771)	White-legged Damselfly	B

Coenagrionidae

Pyrrhosoma nymphula (Sulzer, 1776)	Large Red Damselfly	B
Erythromma najas (Hansemann, 1823)	Red-eyed Damselfly	B
Coenagrion puella (Linnaeus, 1758)	Azure Damselfly	B
Coenagrion pulchellum (van der Linden, 1825)	Variable Damselfly	B
Enallagma cyathigerum (Charpentier, 1840)	Common Blue Damselfly	B
Ischnura pumilio (Charpentier, 1825)	Scarce Blue-tailed Damselfly	Eb
Ischnura elegans (van der Linden, 1820)	Blue-tailed Damselfly	B
Ceriagrion tenellum (Villers, 1789)	Small Red Damselfly	B

SUBORDER Anisoptera

Aeshnidae

Aeshna juncea (Linnaeus, 1758)	Common Hawker	B
Aeshna mixta Latreille, 1805	Migrant Hawker	B+M
Aeshna cyanea (Müller, 1764)	Southern Hawker	B
Aeshna grandis (Linnaeus, 1758)	Brown Hawker	B
Anax imperator Leach, 1815	Emperor Dragonfly	B
Brachytron pratense (Müller, 1764)	Hairy Dragonfly	B

Gomphidae

Gomphus vulgatissimus (Linnaeus, 1758)	Club-tailed Dragonfly	R

Cordulegastridae

Cordulegaster boltonii (Donovan, 1807)	Golden-ringed Dragonfly	B

Corduliidae

Cordulia aenea (Linnaeus, 1758)	Downy Emerald	B
Somatochlora metallica (van der Linden, 1825)	Brilliant Emerald	B

Libellulidae

Libellula quadrimaculata Linnaeus, 1758	Four-spotted Chaser	B+M
Libellula depressa Linnaeus, 1758	Broad-bodied Chaser	B
Orthetrum cancellatum (Linnaeus, 1758)	Black-tailed Skimmer	B
Orthetrum coerulescens (Fabricius, 1798)	Keeled Skimmer	B
Sympetrum striolatum (Charpentier, 1840)	Common Darter	B+M
Sympetrum vulgatum (Linnaeus, 1758)	Vagrant Darter	RV
[*Sympetrum meridionale* (Selys, 1841)	Southern Darter	RV*]
Sympetrum fonscolombii (Selys, 1840)	Red-veined Darter	Mb
Sympetrum flaveolum (Linnaeus, 1758)	Yellow-winged Darter	Mb
Sympetrum sanguineum (Müller, 1764)	Ruddy Darter	B
Sympetrum danae (Sulzer, 1776)	Black Darter	B+M
Leucorrhinia dubia (van der Linden, 1825)	White-faced Darter	B

DISTRIBUTION MAPS

The distribution maps show all the records received for each species or extracted from historical data. They are plotted by tetrad, which is an area 2km by 2km square. A record does not necessarily imply breeding, and therefore may in a few cases indicate only a straggler or wanderer.

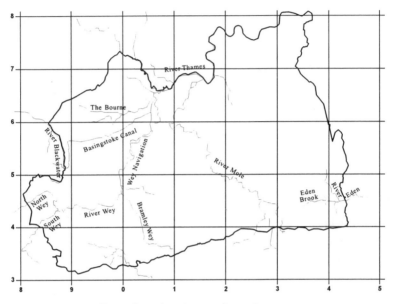

Surrey's major river and canal systems

All the major river and canal systems found within the county are shown on each map, together with the 10km lines of the Ordnance Survey's National Grid; these allow the location of sites in the gazetteer to be found.

Two symbols are used, the black-filled circle for records since 1980 and the open circle for those prior to 1980.

The two following maps show the number of species recorded in each 10km square and the number of tetrads for which records have been obtained, but the lack of any records for a particular tetrad does not mean that dragonflies do not occur there, only that it was not possible to visit it during the current survey.

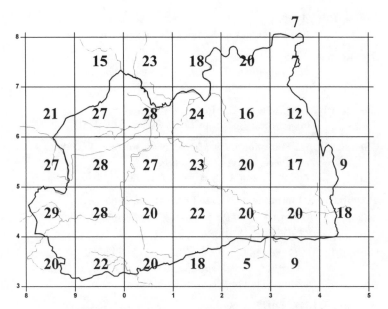

Number of species recorded in each 10km square

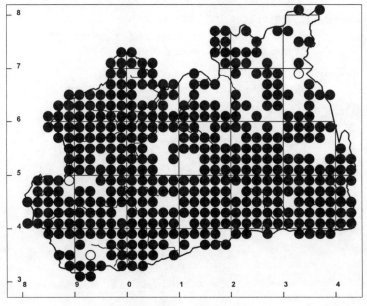

Total records received

FURTHER READING

Askew, R.R., 1988.
The Dragonflies of Europe. Colchester: Harley.

Brooks, S.J., 1989.
The Dragonflies (Odonata) of London: the current status.
The London Naturalist 68: 109-131.

Corbet, P.S., Longfield, C. & Moore, N.W., 1960.
Dragonflies. London: Collins (New Naturalist).

Chelmick, D.G., Hammond, C., Moore, N. & Stubbs, A., 1980.
The Conservation of Dragonflies.
London: Nature Conservancy Council.

d'Aguilar, J., Dommanget, J-L. & Préchac, R., 1986.
A Field Guide to the Dragonflies of Britain, Europe, and North Africa. Collins.

Gibbons, R.B., (1986) 1994.
Dragonflies and Damselflies of Britain and Northern Europe.
London: Hamlyn. (Reprint with corrections.)

Hammond, C.O., (1977) 1983.
Dragonflies of Great Britain and Ireland.
Colchester:Harley. (2nd edition, revised by R.Merritt.)

Longfield, C., (1937) 1949.
The Dragonflies of the British Isles. London and New York:
Warne & Co. (2nd, enlarged edition.)

McGeeney, A., 1986.
A Complete Guide to British Dragonflies. Jonathan Cape.

Merritt, R., Moore, N.W. & Eversham, B.C., 1996.
Atlas of the dragonflies of Britain and Ireland.
Institute of Terrestrial Ecology, Huntingdon.

Miller, P.L., 1987.
Dragonflies. Naturalists' Handbooks 7. Cambridge
University Press. (2nd edition 1996.)

Calopteryx virgo (Linnaeus, 1758)   PLATE 7   Beautiful Demoiselle

National status: local
Total records: 292
Number of tetrads: 93
Breeding status in Surrey:
   confirmed

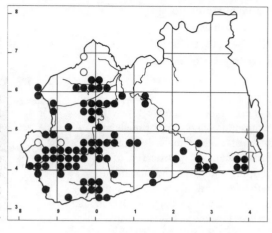

The Beautiful Demoiselle is a fine species with wings an unbanded rich metallic blue in the male and dull purple-brown in the female. It flies slowly with a fluttering flight in and out of vegetation. The male often guards the female during oviposition and is very territorial, frequently chasing away other males.

It is a common species in south-west England and Wales, becoming scarcer in the south-east, since it prefers the faster-flowing streams and rivers with a gravelly substrate, which must be clean and have abundant waterside vegetation with trees giving a degree of shade. It is occasionally found with the Banded Demoiselle but using different stretches of the same water, depending on the bottom condition and water flow. It is also susceptible to clearance of waterside vegetation and canalisation of streams.

In west Surrey it still occurs commonly on the upper reaches of the River Wey and its tributaries, often straying to adjacent commons and woodlands. It also occurs quite commonly on the feeder streams of the River Arun around Dunsfold and Chiddingfold. On these streams it often occurs in thick woodland, congregating in patches of sunlight.

Its status and history in Surrey is a long and fluctuating one, with Lucas (1900) giving records from near Virginia Water, near Farnham, Puttenham Common and on the River Mole near Leatherhead, as indeed did Longfield (1949). But owing to a deterioration in quality of the river water from the mid 1960s onwards, the Beautiful Demoiselle disappeared from the Mole. In the late 1970s it was absent from the eastern half of the county, with the easternmost records being from Vann Lake, where it occurred in quantity on the outflow stream, the North River flowing down into Sussex to join the Arun. At that time it was assumed that the slow-flowing streams and rivers of the weald clay were unsuitable for it, so it was a major surprise when it was recorded by J.B.Steer in 1988 from the Eden Brook below Wire Mill Lake, and by P.Follett in 1993 from a new stretch of the River Mole formed by diverting the river around the new development for Gatwick Airport's North Terminal. Since then it has spread to further sites on the same two river systems, albeit in smaller numbers than elsewhere.

The flight period in Surrey is from May to early August with the earliest record to date being 13th May 1990 by M.Thurner at Bummoor Copse, Compton, and the latest 31st August 1993 by J.Pontin at Mytchett on the Basingstoke Canal.

Calopteryx splendens (Harris, 1782) PLATE 7 **Banded Demoiselle**

National status: local
Total records: 779
Number of tetrads: 169
Breeding status in Surrey:
confirmed

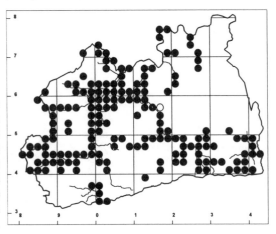

The Banded Demoiselle is a beautiful large damselfly with wings blue-banded in the male and greenish in the female. Its flight is reminiscent of a butterfly, often looping out over the water and returning continually to the same spot. It is one of the few British species to show a courtship display.

It is tolerant of a degree of pollution but is susceptible to vegetation clearance and rapid water movement that can scour the bed and banks of mud and vegetation. It is a widespread and often common species in southern England, where it occurs on slow-flowing streams, rivers and a few lakes, where these have muddy bottoms and plenty of emergent vegetation, often with adjacent water meadows and preferably in direct sun.

In Surrey it has a widespread distribution and is common in most suitable habitats. A glance at the distribution map will show a close correlation with the waterways of the county, where it has had an almost continuous but at times fluctuating existence. Indeed between 1976 and 1980 R.Hawkins found this species to be completely absent from the River Mole above Box Hill. It was present at two sites on a small tributary, the Salfords Brook, and on another tributary stream at Holmethorpe near Redhill, but absent from a third tributary, the Burstow Stream. Local people remembered it, and its disappearance may have been due to canalisation or to river pollution. During the early 1980s it began to spread up river again and was seen at Rice Bridge in 1982. During the hot summers of 1983 and '84, males were frequently seen away from water, even flying along roads in suburban areas. It arrived at Horley on the upper Mole in 1983 and within two years was abundant, but did not return to the Burstow Stream until 1994.

The return of the Banded Demoiselle to the upper Mole may be attributed to improved river quality, perhaps due to the cleaner water being discharged by modern sewage works. Both Gatwick Airport and Crawley New Town, with its large industrial area, drain into the River Mole. There have been several pollution incidents recently and constant vigilance is required from the river authorities, in the detection and prevention of these, to ensure a clean and living river. The presence or absence of damselflies, such as this species and the White-legged Damselfly, may be used as an indicator in this respect.

The Banded Demoiselle was recorded by Lucas (1900) from the River Mole at Esher and Leatherhead, Byfleet, Wisley, Newark Abbey, near Weybridge, Farnham and Send, all sites where it still occurs. Longfield (1949) also described this species as "plentiful", a comment that still applies today.

In Surrey the Banded Demoiselle flies from mid-May to early September, with 7th May 1990 by A.B.Petrie at West End Common being the earliest date and 15th September 1991 by D.&J.Dell at Thursley Common the latest date recorded.

Lestes sponsa (Hansemann, 1823)   PLATE 7   Emerald Damselfly

National status: common
Total records: 728
Number of tetrads: 96
Breeding status in Surrey:
confirmed

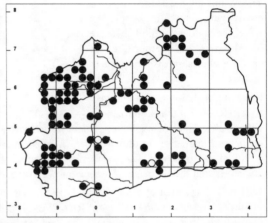

The Emerald Damselfly is a metallic green species with pale powder-blue colouring on segments one and two and at the apex of the abdomen in the male, and a metallic bronze-green robust abdomen in the female.

It is one of the most widespread species in Britain, occurring at sites with an abundance of emergent vegetation, especially sedges and rushes, among which it prefers to fly, rarely venturing out onto the open water. Because of this habit it can be overlooked.

In Surrey it is widespread, occurring in all suitable habitats, and can be extremely abundant, especially on the acid soils of the western heaths. It is a sedentary species that prefers to sit on vegetation for long periods with its wings held slightly open. Pairs have been observed to descend below the water surface to oviposit, usually in tandem and often for long periods.

Although probably always well distributed in the British Isles, there are few early records for the Emerald Damselfly in Surrey. Lucas (1900) mentioned Ockham Common, near Elstead, Chobham Common, Esher Common and Wendlesham. Longfield (1949) stated that "it breeds on all the big Surrey commons with ponds" and gave Esher, Oxshott, West End, Arbrook, Epsom, Ockham and Wimbledon Commons together with Richmond Park and Burgh Heath, all being sites at which it still occurs today.

The Emerald Damselfly is found on the wing in Surrey from mid-June to early September with a peak in August, the earliest record to date being 1st June 1962 by R.M.Fry at Moat Pond, Thursley, and the latest 11th October 1993 by M.Bunce at Richmond Park.

Platycnemis pennipes (Pallas, 1771) PLATE 8 **White-legged Damselfly**

National status: notable/Nb
Total records: 272
Number of tetrads: 76
Breeding status in Surrey:
confirmed; strong widespread
colonies

The White-legged Damselfly is a small, very pale blue species in which the middle and hind tibiae are broad, white and feather-like, for use in a courtship display prior to mating.

Its favoured habitats are sluggish rivers, fenland ditches and canals,

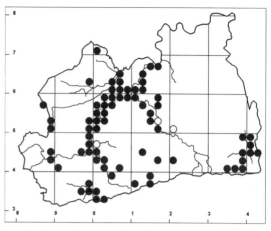

with an abundance of vegetation, where it flies with a weak fluttering flight, often settling on floating plants or, in dull weather, in adjacent meadows. The species is sensitive to pollution and to the removal of waterside vegetation, and also to the canalisation of streams and rivers and the drainage of associated water meadows.

Nationally it is an insect of southern England found only as far north as the south Midlands. In Surrey it occurs commonly on the River Wey Navigation from the Thames to Godalming in the south-west, and less commonly on a small tributary between Bramley and Cranleigh. It also occurs on the River Mole south to Leatherhead, and on a small tributary of the River Arun from Dunsfold to the county border at Alfold. A further stronghold in the county appears to be the River Eden, with the Eden Brook, where there are strong colonies, some in excess of 350 individuals in the Haxted Mill area. Although usually restricted to slow-moving water, it has also been found at a few lake sites, notably Vann Lake, Vachery Pond and Cook's Pond at Dormans Park, together with a clay pit at Ockley and a small pond at Cranleigh. Both Cook's Pond and Vann Lake are hammer ponds formed by damming streams, so water does flow through them in wet seasons, albeit only slowly.

Lucas (1900) gave only Esher Common, Newark Abbey, Ockham Common, Mickleham Downs and near Cobham as localities. Longfield (1949) reported it as "swarming on the rivers Mole and Wey together with the Basingstoke Canal", while Brooks (1989) considered it to be "holding its own on the Mole and Wey".

In Surrey the flight period is from the end of May to early August with the earliest record to date being 22nd May 1995 by J.Silsby on the River Eden at Haxted, the latest 18th August 1991 by M.Thurner at Shalford Marsh.

Pyrrhosoma nymphula (Sulzer, 1776)   PLATE 8   Large Red Damselfly

National status: common
Total records: 1185
Number of tetrads: 214
Breeding status in Surrey:
confirmed; widespread except
in north-east

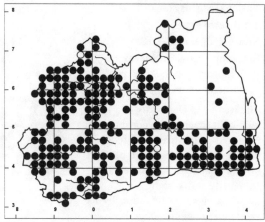

The Large Red Damselfly is a
sturdy red damselfly with black legs
and is only possibly confused with
the Small Red Damselfly, a smaller
species with pale red legs, which is
found mainly on the western heaths.

This species is generally common
throughout the British Isles and has
a wide habitat tolerance, being found in small garden ponds as well as large lakes, rivers
and canals, and also being tolerant of acid or mildly polluted waters.

In Surrey it can be extremely common and is generally widespread, with the exception of
the north-east of the county where it is scarce. Its numbers can fluctuate, especially when
bad weather early in the flight period drastically reduces populations. Fresh insects appear
in late summer when the main flush of May emergents has disappeared. These may
represent a second generation, or perhaps are just late developers.

Lucas (1900) had records from near the River Mole at Esher, Esher Common, near Byfleet,
near Chobham Common, near Send, the River Wey at Wisley, Ockham Common, Ripley,
and near Weybridge.

It is usually the first species to emerge in the spring, with the earliest record to date being
30th March 1991 by D.&J.Dell at The Hatches and the latest 29th August 1991 by
D.&J.Dell at Englemere.

Erythromma najas (Hansemann, 1823)   PLATE 8   Red-eyed Damselfly

National status: local
Total records: 857
Number of tetrads: 128
Breeding status in Surrey:
confirmed, with some very
large colonies

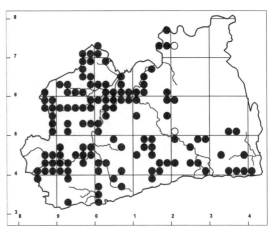

The Red-eyed Damselfly is a large
well-built species with conspicuous
eyes, red in the male and reddish-
brown in the female. It bears a
similarity to the Blue-tailed
Damselfly at first sight, but is given
away on closer observation by its
size and eye-colour, together with
a strong flight.

This attractive species is rather local in south-central and south-east England, the Midlands and the Welsh borders, breeding in lakes, large ponds, wide ditches and canals. It favours those with plenty of emergent plants, especially water-lilies and pondweeds. It rests on these, usually as far from the shore as possible, and flies low and strongly from patch to patch.

In Surrey it is now a common and widespread species, except in the north-east, occurring on almost every large pond, lake, canal and those reaches of slow-flowing rivers with emergent vegetation. It appears to be increasing its range, since Lucas (1900) only gave six localities: Ockham, Esher and Chobham Commons, Richmond Park, Virginia Water and near Byfleet. Longfield (1949) stated that it was "plentiful and breeding on most of the commons and lakes", a situation that exists today with some sites holding enormous populations, as at Vann Lake where in July 1993 over 3,000 were counted on a single visit.

This is a fairly early species, on the wing in Surrey from mid-May to early September with a suspicion of two peaks, June and August. The earliest record is 13th May 1993 by P.&S.Follett at Black Pond, Esher Common, and the latest 17th September 1992 by D.&J.Dell at Henleypark Lake.

Coenagrion puella (Linnaeus, 1758)   PLATE 9   Azure Damselfly

National status: common
Total records: 1523
Number of tetrads: 262
Breeding status in Surrey:
    confirmed, very common

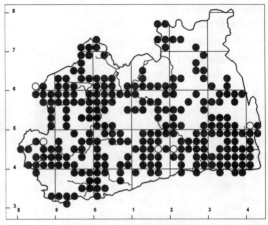

The male Azure Damselfly is predominantly blue with a somewhat variable U-shaped black mark on segment two of the abdomen, narrow blue thoracic stripes and a black thoracic spur. It flies low and settles frequently on both standing and floating vegetation. When egg-laying 'in tandem' with the male, the female has been observed to submerge itself completely for long periods, on one occasion for sixteen minutes at Vann Lake reserve.

Nationally this is another very common and widespread species in England and Wales but is scarce in Scotland. It is not as tolerant of pollution as the Blue-tailed Damselfly, but breeds in all types of still and flowing water such as lakes, ponds, ditches, bogs and slow-flowing rivers, provided that there is abundant emergent vegetation. It prefers the more sheltered areas out of the wind, where sometimes very large numbers can occur. It is also a typical species of small garden ponds, and is often one of the first colonisers of new ponds.

It is found very commonly throughout the county, even in the heavily built-up areas of London, where it occurs at Wimbledon Common, Croydon and Putney Heath.

This is another early emergent in spring, with the earliest date being 29th April 1993 by D.&J.Dell on the Basingstoke Canal at Ash, and the latest 23rd September 1978 by R.Hawkins at Durkins Pond, south of Dormans Park.

Coenagrion pulchellum (van der Linden, 1825) PLATE 9 **Variable Damselfly**

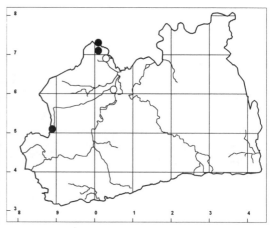

National status: notable/Nb

Total records: 21

Number of tetrads: 5

Breeding status in Surrey:
confirmed, very local

The Variable Damselfly is another blue species, easily confused with the Azure Damselfly in the field, but distinctive in the hand from a combination of the three-lobed posterior margin of the prothorax (more pronounced in the female), the wine-goblet-shaped mark on the second abdominal segment, the broken thoracic stripes looking like an exclamation mark, and the shape of the terminal genitalia. As the name suggests, it is variable in its markings, so can easily be overlooked.

In England and Wales it is a widespread but scarce species and has recently been found in Scotland, but generally it appears to be in decline, possibly due to deterioration of its habitat, which is water meadows and levels with clear unpolluted streams, ditches, dykes and ponds.

This damselfly has probably always been rare in Surrey, as Lucas (1900) only gave the Basingstoke Canal at Byfleet, while Longfield (1949) added Weybridge. D.Baldock found it swarming at an old, disused gravel-pit between Staines and Chertsey in 1978, and in good numbers in 1975 at Langhams Pond at Runnymede where it is still common today. A further site on the Basingstoke Canal at Ash has recently been discovered, so continued careful and methodical recording may yet produce more sites.

The earliest record is 9th June 1992 by D.&J.Dell at Langhams Pond, Runnymede, and the latest 4th August 1975 by D.Baldock at the same locality.

Enallagma cyathigerum (Charpentier, 1840) PLATE 9 **Common Blue Damselfly**

National status: common
Total records: 1616
Number of tetrads: 229
Breeding status in Surrey:
  confirmed, abundant

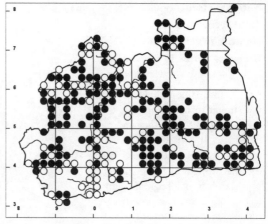

The Common Blue Damselfly is a robust blue damselfly often seen in large numbers flying over open water. The male is best distinguished from other similar 'blue damselflies' by the blue eighth and ninth abdominal segments and a black mushroom-shaped mark on the second segment, whereas the female is a dull greenish or blue colour with a distinctive spine on the underside of segment eight. It can be very aggressive towards other species and has been observed driving off the Red-eyed Damselfly, a species larger than itself.

It breeds in all types of still and slow-flowing water, usually where there is abundant marginal and floating vegetation, but is also found in recently-flooded sand and gravel pits with rather bare banks, such as the Godstone Reservoirs. In such habitats it can be the dominant damselfly species. It will also fly in strong winds, being one of the few species to do so. It does not however seem to tolerate pollution quite as well as the Blue-tailed Damselfly.

It is found throughout the county, even in the heavily built-up areas of the north and north-east such as Kew Gardens, Dulwich, Putney Heath, Wandsworth and Southwark. Its status has changed little since Lucas (1900) gave Richmond Park, Esher, Ockham, Chobham and Bookham Commons, near Pyrford, near Byfleet, Merton and Weybridge as localities for this species. Longfield (1949) described it as "exceedingly common in almost all the counties in the British Isles".

The flight period in Surrey for this common and widespread species is from mid-May to mid-September, with the earliest record to date being 3rd May 1993 by D.Tagg at Thursley Common, the latest 31st October 1995 by D.Tagg at Moat Pond, Thursley.

Ischnura pumilio (Charpentier, 1825) PLATE 10 **Scarce Blue-tailed Damselfly**

National status: notable/Nb

Total records: 2

Number of tetrads: 1

Breeding status in Surrey: not now known to breed

The Scarce Blue-tailed Damselfly is a similar insect to the Blue-tailed Damselfly, but is smaller and more delicate. It can be difficult to identify except in the hand where its anal appendages and all-blue ninth abdominal segment can be examined. There is a bright orange female form *aurantiaca* (Selys).

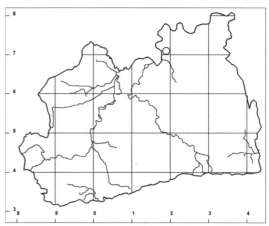

The species is thought to be dispersed by wind currents and appears to be spreading eastwards from its mainly western localities in Britain (Cham, 1991).

It has not been recorded in Surrey since 1932 when it was found in some numbers by H.G.Attlee in Richmond Park, in a little boggy runnel at the corner of a pond near Kingston Hill Gate. Unfortunately this bog was piped in 1933 and the site became unsuitable. It was only discovered there in 1931, being unknown to Lucas in Surrey.

It is found in small runnels, either acidic or alkaline, so there appears to be plenty of suitable habitat left in Surrey for the species to colonise, especially as it is found in the adjoining counties of Hampshire and Berkshire.

Ischnura elegans (van der Linden, 1820) PLATE 10 **Blue-tailed Damselfly**

National status: common

Total records: 1754

Number of tetrads: 264

Breeding status in Surrey: confirmed

The Blue-tailed Damselfly is a small species, noted for the colour variations in the female. It is probably our commonest species, being found throughout the British Isles, but at a lower density in northern England and Scotland. It has a preference for well vegetated and more sheltered sites.

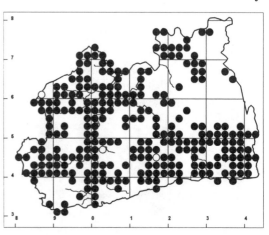

In Surrey, it is the most common and widespread species, occurring on almost every stretch of water, still or moving, often in abundance. It seems able to tolerate pollution more than other species and is often the only one to be found on heavily polluted waters. It even occurs and probably breeds in central London, the only damselfly to do so apart from the Common Blue Damselfly.

Being so common, there are very few references to this species in the literature for Surrey, but Lucas (1900) gave Ockham, Chobham, Wimbledon and Esher Commons, Merton, canal near Byfleet, near Send, Richmond Park, Kew Gardens and Virginia Water.

The Blue-tailed Damselfly has a long season, flying from mid-May to early September, the earliest record to date being 1st May 1993 by D.&J.Dell at Ash on the Basingstoke Canal, the latest 20th September 1988 by R.Hawkins at Bay Pond, a Surrey Wildlife Trust reserve.

Ceriagrion tenellum (Villers, 1789)   PLATE 10   **Small Red Damselfly**

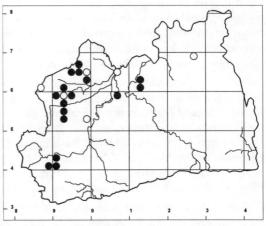

National status: notable/Nb

Total records: 203

Number of tetrads: 22

Breeding status in Surrey:
confirmed; mainly on western heaths

The Small Red Damselfly, with red or yellowish-brown legs and a feeble flight, has a predominantly Mediterranean distribution. It occurs in Britain on peat bogs and wet heaths in the south and south-west of England, and locally in Wales, with a scattering of mainly old records from Suffolk and Norfolk (Mendel, 1992), and from the east Midlands.

It is a very local species, not moving far from its breeding sites where it can sometimes occur in large numbers, as on Thursley Common. In Surrey it is still found at some twelve sites, notably Thursley, Chobham Common, Henleypark Lake and Gracious Pond, all in the west of the county, and all on boggy heathland.

Lucas (1900) had records of this species from Ockham and Esher Commons, Richmond Park, Virginia Water and near Byfleet, but unfortunately it has now gone from all of them. In 1948 Longfield described it as "abundant on several commons outside the London area and sparingly within the London area, and that early in the century it was plentiful on Esher Common" (Longfield, 1949). At Esher it occurred on bog pools in the open heathland until the late 1970s when unfortunately the heath became afforested.

The flight period in Surrey is from June to mid-September with a peak in July, the earliest record to date being 25th May 1963 by R.M.Fry at the Moat Pond, Thursley, and the latest 17th September 1992 by D.&J.Dell at Thursley Bog.

Aeshna juncea (Linnaeus, 1758)   PLATE 11   **Common Hawker**

National status: common
Total records: 214
Number of tetrads: 45
Breeding status in Surrey:
  confirmed, local

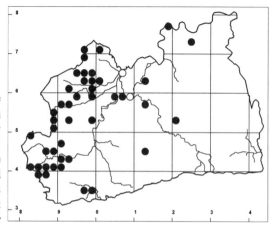

The Common Hawker is a large blackish-brown dragonfly with yellow costal veins and no yellow triangle on segment two. All segments of the abdomen have spots, blue in the male and yellowish-green in the female. Its flight is often low down amongst marginal vegetation when near water, but it is also found along rides in woods, sometimes until dusk or even later if the weather is warm. It is a very active species, except when the weather is cloudy or wet, and when mating, which can take several hours.

Nationally it is a species with a preference for heaths and moorland. It is common in the north and west but more local in the Midlands and south-east. In Surrey the Common Hawker is found on the heaths and bogs in the west of the county, but is nowhere as common as its name suggests, and is much scarcer than the Southern Hawker. Strongholds for this species include Thursley, Basingstoke Canal, Henleypark Lake, Chobham Common, Bolder Mere and Esher Common. As it is difficult to differentiate from the Southern Hawker, its status in Surrey will require continued monitoring by experienced recorders, especially in those localities, on acid soils, where there are strong colonies.

This has never been a widespread species in the county. Lucas (1900) only gave Ockham Common, near Elstead, Weybridge and Esher Common, from where on 15th September 1896 eggs were extracted from the dead body of a female. Longfield (1949) stated that "it breeds regularly on a few of the Surrey Commons", but did not include any sites, whereas Brooks (1989) gave Wimbledon and Esher Commons.

The main flight period in Surrey is from July to early October with the earliest date being 10th June 1965 at Pudmore Pond, Thursley Common, by R.M.Fry and the latest 15th October 1991 at Windsor Great Park by D.&J.Dell.

Aeshna mixta Latreille, 1805   PLATE 11   **Migrant Hawker**

National status: local
Total records: 739
Number of tetrads:152
Breeding status in Surrey:
  confirmed, widespread

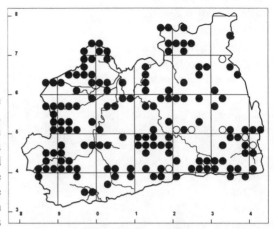

The Migrant Hawker is one of the smaller hawker dragonflies, appearing very dark in flight from its dark-brown abdomen with a yellow triangle on segment two and paired blue spots on all the remaining segments in mature males; these spots are lilac-blue in immature males. The female is similar but with dull greenish-blue markings. Both sexes have long anal appendages and brown costal veins, not yellow as in the Common Hawker.

This species has a strong flight, hovers frequently and will fly from early morning until dusk on warm sunny days. It is often found feeding in groups away from water along woodland rides and pathways and is less territorial than other *Aeshna* species. As its name suggests, this is a migrant species, with a Mediterranean distribution in Europe, that has slowly moved northwards, increasing its breeding range, to become well established in southern England up to the Midlands and East Anglia. Indeed Longfield, in response to a challenge to prove breeding of this species in the British Isles, published an article summarising the proven breeding records up to 1948 that showed Surrey to be in the forefront of this range extension (Longfield, 1949b).

The habitats of the Migrant Hawker are reservoirs, lakes, ponds, gravel-pits, slow-moving rivers and canals, with good marginal vegetation and adjoining shelter being important. In Surrey this is a fairly common and widespread species found in all suitable sites, but fluctuating in numbers year by year, possibly due more to fresh immigration than to local breeding success. It can sometimes be seen in large aggregations of twenty or more in sheltered spots in woods. It breeds in sites across the county from Newdigate Brickworks and Vann Lake in the south to Wimbledon Common, Chobham Common and the Basingstoke Canal in the north and west.

Lucas (1900) gave Esher Common (scarce) and Ockham Common, from where he caught a female on 11th September 1897 and extracted the eggs that were used in the description in his book. Longfield (1949) gave the Basingstoke Canal, Esher and Oxshott Commons, and later (1949b) added Newdigate, Wisley Pond, Richmond Park, Mytchett Lake and the "Surrey commons", all sites with post-1985 records.

The main flight period of this species in Surrey is from August to October, being one of the last species to appear in the year. The earliest date is 15th July 1983 by R.B.Hastings at Kew Gardens and the latest 27th November 1994 by W.Whitaker at Crooksbury Common.

Aeshna cyanea (Müller, 1764)   PLATE 11   Southern Hawker

National status: common
Total records: 905
Number of tetrads: 213
Breeding status in Surrey:
  confirmed, widespread

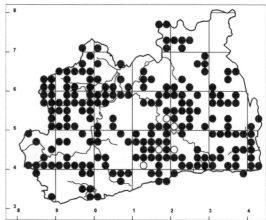

The Southern Hawker is a large dragonfly with two broad green thoracic stripes and greenish-blue spots on all abdominal segments except nine and ten which have bands, blue in the male but green in the female, making it a very beautiful insect.

It is a rather inquisitive species that will often approach the observer and has been known to oviposit in clothing. Indeed it is noted for unusual oviposition sites such as brick walls, concrete, soil, rotting logs, among tree roots and even into a shoe on one occasion.

It has a strong, high flight, settling often, and will fly quite late in the evening if the weather is suitable, such as in 1992 when seen at a porch light consuming a cranefly. Males can be very aggressive when on their breeding territories, which include lakes, canals, clay-pits, gravel-pits and garden ponds, ranging from acidic to alkaline. It is often seen feeding away from water along woodland rides and hedgerows, and over fields and open downland. It is a partial migrant and appears to be extending its range northwards in the British Isles, having recently reached Scotland. It is a common and widespread species in the southern counties of England.

In Surrey the Southern Hawker is found on all the waters detailed above, as well as slow-moving stretches of rivers such as the Mole and Wey, and some of the bog pools on the heathland at Thursley. It is a common and widespread species, being even found in the heavily built-up area of north-east Surrey now within the political boundaries of London. For instance, it has been recorded at Kew Gardens and along the River Thames towpath, but it is a well-known wanderer and is often seen well away from water.

Historically, there are records in Lucas (1900) from Purley, Kingston-on-Thames where on "October 24th, 1897 one was taken from a gutter", Chertsey, Esher Common, near Claygate, Ockham Common and Weybridge. Longfield (1949) recorded this species as "extremely common and widespread", which is still the situation today.

The flight period in Surrey is from July to early October with the earliest being 23rd June 1993 by D.&J.Dell at Normandy Pond, the latest 16th December 1986 by J.Silsby at Purley. The latter is an exceptionally late date.

Aeshna grandis (Linnaeus, 1758)   PLATE 12   **Brown Hawker**

National status: common
Total records: 1296
Number of tetrads: 245
Breeding status in Surrey:
    confirmed, abundant

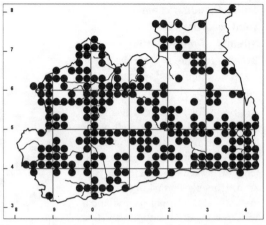

The Brown Hawker is a large dark-brown dragonfly with amber-coloured wings, making it an easily identified species in Surrey. It flies powerfully from dawn until dusk on warm summer evenings, settling often, but is very wary and easily disturbed. As a wanderer and suspected migrant, it is often one of the first colonisers of newly-excavated mineral workings, as soon as there is a growth of emergent and marginal vegetation.

Its preferred habitats are lakes, slow-flowing rivers, canals and large ponds with good marginal vegetation and clear water. It can often be found in the heart of towns and built-up areas. This species oviposits singly, without the male, into mud, plants or rotted wood, but has been seen to oviposit, in a group of nine females, into a five-foot long floating log on the Basingstoke Canal.

Nationally it is a common species in the south and northwards to southern Yorkshire, but is scarce in the south-west, Wales and the extreme north of England, and absent from Scotland. In Surrey this is our commonest *Aeshna*, found throughout the county on all suitable waters, and has even been found along the scarp slope of the North Downs flying along the hedgerows and over the short grass swards, far from any water.

Lucas (1900) gave Esher and Ockham Commons, near Clandon, near Byfleet, near Chobham, Kew, Weybridge, Bookham Common and Richmond Park from where he caught a female on 11th September 1898. He extracted the eggs and these were used in describing the egg in his book. Longfield (1949) described it as abundant.

The main flight period of the Brown Hawker in Surrey is from late June to the end of September, or early October in a good year with suitable weather, the earliest date being 9th June 1992 at Thursley Common by M.Thurner, the latest 11th October 1986 at the Stew Pond, Epsom Common, also by M.Thurner.

Anax imperator Leach, 1815   PLATE 12   **Emperor Dragonfly**

National status: common
Total records: 959
Number of tetrads: 192
Breeding status in Surrey:
  confirmed, common

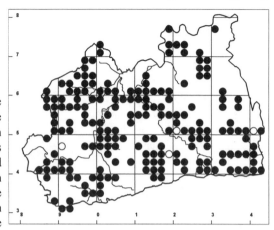

The Emperor Dragonfly is a large and beautiful hawker with a blue abdomen and black dorsal stripe in the mature male. The abdomen is green in immature males and females, but with age the female can attain the blue markings of the mature male. In flight its abdomen appears curved, not straight as in the *Aeshna* species. Males are very territorial and patrol their breeding sites continually from early morning until dusk in good weather, frequently clashing with any intruders. They rarely settle except to devour prey items that can be as large as a butterfly or even another dragonfly or damselfly.

Nationally it occurs in the south of England from about the Severn to the Wash and in south Wales, but is rare elsewhere and absent from northern parts of Britain. The species requires a large territory, so is usually found on the larger stretches of water such as lakes, large ponds, canals, gravel-pits, reservoirs and slow-flowing rivers and streams. Individuals do occasionally visit the smaller ponds, for example a female laying eggs at a small garden pond in Horley in 1992.

In Surrey it is very common and widespread, being found on all suitable waters from acidic bog-pools to ponds on the weald clay. It has a synchronised emergence that takes place during the hours of darkness (Corbet, 1962), often in large numbers at favoured sites. One such site, a small lake at Broomhall Heath, Wentworth, produced 76 exuviae on a single early morning visit during 1994, but only one adult male and two ovipositing females were seen.

Lucas (1900) gave the following sites: Ockham Common, immature on 15th May 1893; Esher Common (fairly plentiful), adults on 10th August 1894, exuviae on 17th and 21st June 1897, and a female on 18th July 1897; Chobham, Bookham, and Crooksbury Commons, and near Byfleet. Longfield (1949) gave many sites including Wimbledon Common, Croydon, Epsom and Ranmore Commons, Richmond Park, Kew Gardens and Putney Heath. All these sites have produced up-to-date breeding records during the course of the current survey, except for Kew and Putney Heath, with only sight records.

The Emperor Dragonfly emerges early in the spring and in Surrey the flight period is from mid-May to early September, with the earliest date being 19th May 1990 at Chiddingfold by M.Thurner, the latest 27th September 1995 at Frensham Great Pond by D.&J.Dell.

Brachytron pratense (Müller, 1764)   PLATE 12   Hairy Dragonfly

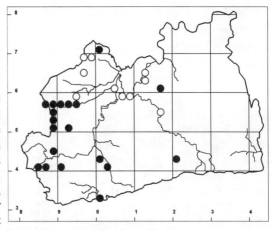

National status: notable/Nb
Total records: 150
Number of tetrads: 29
Breeding status in Surrey:
  confirmed, local

The Hairy Dragonfly is one of the smallest hawker dragonflies, with blue dots along the abdomen in the male and smaller yellowish ones in the female, together with a distinctly hairy thorax in both sexes. Owing to its very early flight period, confusion with other similar dragonflies is unlikely, except towards the end of its season when the *Aeshna* species begin to fly.

It flies low over the water and among reeds and other tall herbage, in sunshine, settling often when the weather is changeable. The preferred habitats of this species are the coastal marshes and levels, and the canals and dykes of fenlands. In Britain it is found mainly in the south-west, the south and along the East Anglian coast together with the Broads in Norfolk; elsewhere it is very scarce and widely scattered. The species appears to be decreasing in Britain, mainly because of habitat loss with the steady reclaiming of marshland and coastal levels, and it has become a vulnerable species nationally.

In Surrey its stronghold is the Basingstoke Canal where in some years it can be common on suitable stretches and adjacent lakes. Other localities include Runnymede, Sidney Wood near Dunsfold, Frensham Little Pond and Thundry Meadows nature reserve. It may also breed in stretches of the old Wey and Arun Canal around Bramley, since odd specimens have been seen there in recent years.

The history of this species in Surrey is one of fluctuation as Lucas (1900) gave six locations: River Mole at Esher, Byfleet, Ockham Common, Leatherhead, Bisley and Egham. Longfield (1949) only gave three: Esher and Bookham Commons and the Basingstoke Canal. D.Baldock in his 1970-1980 survey only gave Frensham Little Pond. This compares with 17 regularly recorded sites in the county during the current survey, plus other odd occurrences. Hopefully this indicates a small revival in its fortunes, but close monitoring of sites and numbers should be a continuing priority.

The flight period in Surrey is from May to early July with the earliest date being 1st May 1993 by D.&J.Dell on the Basingstoke Canal at Ash, the latest 5th July 1991 by D.&J.Dell at Langhams Pond, Runnymede.

Gomphus vulgatissimus (Linnaeus, 1758)   PLATE 13   **Club-tailed Dragonfly**

National status: notable/Nb
Total records: 5
Number of tetrads: 5
Breeding status in Surrey: not
   breeding, straggler

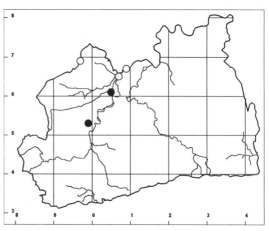

The Club-tailed Dragonfly, with its black and yellowish-green markings and distinctive club-shaped tail, is unlikely to be confused with any of the other medium-sized dragonflies in Britain. It is a species with a distinctly riverine habitat, where it flies slowly, hovering and settling frequently, which makes it difficult to spot. It is a very local species found mainly on the rivers Thames, Wye, Severn, and Arun in West Sussex, with a breeding site only five miles from the Surrey border.

The species is thought to be declining and is in need of close monitoring and study in order to ascertain its true status and distribution in Britain. It can be elusive, even in its known sites, possibly due to its habit of spending most of the time away from water among trees and bushes and, in the case of the female, only coming to water to pair and oviposit.

It is only a very rare straggler in the county with just five records. The first was at Weybridge on the Thames in 1871 by McLachlan and the second by A.B.Higgs at Walton-on-Thames in 1900 (Lucas, 1902), both probably washed down as nymphs from breeding sites further up the river in Berkshire, where it still occurs. There were no further records until 2nd June 1965 at Virginia Water by J.Pontin, June 1990 by F.Greenaway at West Byfleet, and most recently a female at Whitmoor Common on 8th June 1993, which was watched for about half an hour by D.Tagg. The last may possibly have been a wanderer from a site on the River Arun, only 20 miles away to the south-east.

Because it is so elusive, with colonies still being found in unexpected places, it is just possible for it to be breeding in Surrey, especially along the county border with Sussex on tributaries of the River Arun.

Cordulegaster boltonii (Donovan, 1807) PLATE 13 Golden-ringed Dragonfly

National status: common/Nr
Total records: 155
Number of tetrads: 35
Breeding status in Surrey:
confirmed; strong colonies

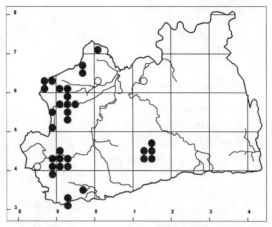

The Golden-ringed Dragonfly is a large black-and-yellow hawker with a slightly club-shaped abdomen with yellow bands, which gives this species its common name. The female, with her long ovipositor, is the longest-bodied British dragonfly.

This species has a strong preference for acidic waters, often ponds and lakes on heathland but more usually those small streams running through boggy heaths and moorland that are fairly fast and well-oxygenated. It is often found away from breeding sites feeding in woodland or over vegetation, especially early or late in the day. It then comes to water, selecting a particular stretch to patrol, and proceeds to fly strongly and low above the water until it meets a female which is grasped and, after mating, released to implant her eggs firmly into the mud or gravel substrate.

In Britain this is a dragonfly of the heaths and moors in west and south-west England, Wales, Cumbria and north-west Scotland. It is found more locally in the Pennines and Midlands, together with small colonies on the heathlands of south and south-east England.

The Golden-ringed Dragonfly is found in Surrey in what appears to be two distinct areas, namely, the heathy and often boggy areas in the west and on the small streams draining from the sandstone ridge around Leith Hill, where, together with Thursley, it occurs in its greatest abundance. An experiment, undertaken during 1994 at Leith Hill on the upper reaches of the Tillingbourne, using the capture and marking of specimens, produced figures of ten males and nine females on 25th July within a 500-metre stretch of the stream. This excluded further specimens flying over an adjacent pond. Other sites include the Basingstoke Canal, the new National Nature Reserve at Chobham Common, Pirbright Ranges and West End Common.

There have also been occasional recent sightings of singletons in the woods along the Sussex border around Lythe Hill and in Tugley Wood. There is a possibility of another breeding colony to be discovered in this area, although the habitat does not appear to be right. However they may only be wanderers from colonies over the border in Sussex or Hampshire.

It is unclear yet whether this species has increased in Surrey or whether the level of recording has led to a clearer understanding of the distribution in the county, since Lucas (1900) only gave Ottershaw as a location. Longfield (1949) gave Wimbledon Common, Esher

Common (a dying female in 1900), Richmond Park and as "an abundant resident of the commons further south".

The flight period in Surrey is from early June to mid-September with the earliest record being 28th May 1994 by P.Beuk at Elstead Bridge, the latest 4th October 1993 by D.&J.Dell at Thursley.

Cordulia aenea (Linnaeus, 1758)   PLATE 13   Downy Emerald

National status: notable/Nb
Total records: 619
Number of tetrads: 94
Breeding status in Surrey:
   confirmed, widespread

The Downy Emerald is a small dark bronze-green dragonfly with a downy thorax, bright green eyes, and a clubbed and slightly drooping tip to the abdomen in the male. The males patrol regular beats low down along the water's edge, hovering in favoured spots, whereas the females are more commonly found along

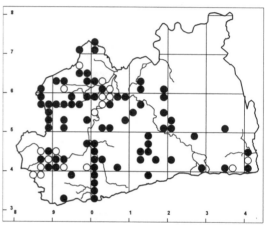

woodland rides, except when coming to water to mate and oviposit. This the female does alone, by striking the surface of the water and releasing clusters of eggs. It is an early spring species and is often seen flying late in the evening in suitable weather.

Nationally it is a very local species, found in scattered localities in western Britain, north to Scotland and locally common south of the Thames. It may be found at sheltered woodland ponds, lakes, canals, streams and quiet stretches of rivers, ranging from acidic to alkaline.

This species is a Surrey speciality, being found more commonly here than in any other county. Indeed it is one of the commonest of the early summer dragonflies, being found in such diverse habitats as old clay and gravel-pits, small lakes, canals and slow-moving rivers such as the Basingstoke Canal and River Wey, and heathland bogs such as Thursley. However it does not occur in the north-east of the county. Due to this species' abundance in Surrey, it is strange that it is not more common and widespread in other parts of the country. Hopefully, further study of the Downy Emerald's ecological requirements will explain this phenomenon.

Lucas (1900) gave only Esher Common, near Byfleet, Ockham Common and Bookham Common (C.A.Briggs). Harcourt-Bath (1890) gave Godalming as a further locality. Longfield (1949) gave Black Pond at Esher, Epsom Stew Ponds and the Basingstoke Canal between Weybridge and Basingstoke as regular breeding sites, and Richmond Park, Wimbledon Common and Bookham Common as "breeding sparingly". She also commented that it is "definitely increasing as a breeding species". Brooks (1989), in his survey of the London area, also gives Epsom and Esher Commons.

In Surrey the flight period of this species extends from May to mid-August in normal years with the earliest record being 2nd May 1994 by D.&J.Dell at Normandy Pond, the latest 13th September 1891 by C.A.Briggs at Bookham Common, which compares well with one on 8th September 1991 by J.Dell and S.M.Guy at Thursley Moat Pond.

Somatochlora metallica (van der Linden, 1825) PLATE 13 **Brilliant Emerald**

National status: notable/Nb

Total records: 346

Number of tetrads: 60

Breeding status in Surrey:
    confirmed, local

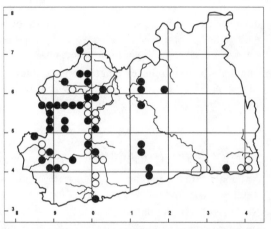

The Brilliant Emerald is slightly larger than the Downy Emerald and has a bright metallic-green abdomen and thorax; the latter is slightly downy and the head has a U-shaped yellow mark across the frons and bright green eyes. The males have a distinctly waisted abdomen at segments three and four. They fly with a level abdomen and drooping anal appendages on a regular beat along the water's edge, often under overhanging vegetation, especially alder trees, provided that the cover is not too dense and there is plenty of light. Females are often to be found flying high along woodland rides. They only come to water to mate and oviposit, which they usually do directly into mud, sphagnum or other substrate, often with vigorous thrusts of the abdomen. This is a species with a preference for still waters and canals, or those quiet sections of slow-flowing rivers and streams with plenty of water-side vegetation.

Nationally the Brilliant Emerald has a very strange disjunct distribution, being found only in Scotland and in southern central England. It is one of the specialities of Surrey, being found here more commonly than in any other county. It occurs predominantly in the western half of the county and around the sandstone ridge at Leith Hill. The distribution of this species extends into neighbouring counties. It is found extensively in the High Weald of Sussex, and this area of distribution just extends to a few sites in south-east Surrey, such as Cook's Pond at Dormans Park, Hedgecourt Lake and along the Eden Brook. However it is a much rarer species than the Downy Emerald, and is hardly ever seen more than one or two at a time. Strongholds for this species are the Basingstoke Canal, Thursley Common, Chobham Common, the southern stretches of the River Wey, Esher Common and Leith Hill.

It seems that the Brilliant Emerald has either only colonised southern England in this century, or was previously unrecognised, since Lucas stated in 1900 that "it is only to be found in Scotland". By 1947 Longfield said that it was "known from rather few sites in the British Isles and only one in Surrey, the Basingstoke Canal", and in 1949 could only add

Wisley Common. In fact it had been recorded in 1939 by H.G.Attlee and A.W.Richards on Thursley Common. It still occurs in all these three locations. Longfield further reported that it had been seen on the canal at Byfleet in 1954, and D.Baldock had records from 29 localities by 1975. Brooks (1989) gave Esher and Fairmile Commons together with Bookham.

Reference to the map will show that there are now almost 40 sites in the county where this species has occurred since 1980, many with breeding records. It may well still occur at most of the pre-1980 sites on the map, making a possible total of about 60 sites. It is therefore either increasing steadily or has been overlooked in the past. But whatever the reason, the Brilliant Emerald is a species that must be closely monitored in order to answer some of the ecological questions posed, and to ensure its continued success in Surrey.

The flight period in Surrey ranges from late May to the end of August, with the earliest date being 20th May 1990 by A.S.Gray at Thursley Common, the latest 14th September 1991 by S.M.Guy at Pirbright on the Basingstoke Canal.

Libellula quadrimaculata Linnaeus, 1758   PLATE 13   **Four-spotted Chaser**

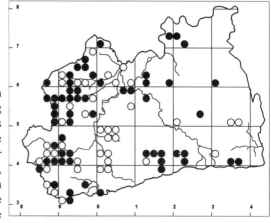

National status: common
Total records: 680
Number of tetrads: 98
Breeding status in Surrey:
  confirmed

The male and female are similar in the Four-spotted Chaser, being yellowish-brown with yellow marks on the sides of the abdomen. The distinctive wings have four additional brown spots at the nodes, which give this species its common name. Males are very aggressive and territorial, especially in the morning, when they occupy a perch from where they guard their territories and look for visiting females, which spend most of their time away from water.

This is an early species favouring lakes, ponds, canals and other waters, mainly still. Its habitats range from brackish to acidic, but it is found most commonly at heathland pools. Since it is a noted migrant, it is sometimes difficult to decide whether it has bred at a site or arrived as a result of migration from the continent, where sometimes very large movements occur. In Britain it is fairly widespread and often common, especially in the west and south, becoming much scarcer in the east and north-east, but fairly widespread in Scotland.

In Surrey the Four-spotted Chaser is common and sometimes abundant on lakes, ponds, bogs and marshes in the west, but decidedly uncommon in the east, with only a few sites, mainly in the south-east such as Hedgecourt Lake, the disused brickworks at Newdigate (very common), and Wire Mill Lake at Felbridge. It still occurs at Esher and Epsom Commons, Wimbledon Common and Richmond Park in the north of the county.

Lucas (1900) used illustrations from Surrey-caught specimens in his book 'British Dragonflies' and gave Esher Common (with a specimen taken on 25th April 1894), Byfleet, Ockham Common, Chobham Common and Weybridge as localities for this species. Longfield (1949) stated that "it is Surrey that undoubtedly receives the bulk of the immigrants and also has the largest breeding population in the London area", and gave Black Pond at Esher Common, Epsom, Wimbledon Common, Bookham and the Basingstoke Canal, all sites where the Four-spotted Chaser is still found.

It is on the wing in Surrey from the beginning of May until the first few days of September, the earliest date this century being 1st May 1993 at Thursley Common by S.Price, and the latest 20th September 1991 by D.&J.Dell, also at Thursley.

Libellula depressa Linnaeus, 1758   PLATE 14   Broad-bodied Chaser

National status: common
Total records: 610
Number of tetrads: 156
Breeding status in Surrey:
confirmed, widespread and common

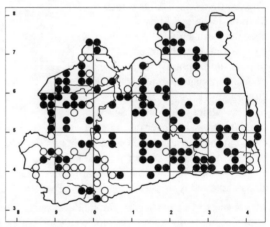

The Broad-bodied Chaser has a very broad abdomen with yellow spots along the sides. It is coloured powder-blue in the mature male but brown in the immature male and female. Dark brown wing-bases also serve to identify this species. Males are aggressive and territorial, flying from a prominent perch to intercept intruders. Females oviposit alone, with the male in close attendance, but are often observed away from breeding sites flying along hedgerows and woodland rides. This is an early coloniser of newly-created habitats such as gravel-pits and ponds, with bare edges. In Surrey it is also found on well-vegetated ponds, lakes, ditches, canals and slow-flowing sheltered sections of rivers. It is often found in garden ponds, some being quite small, and these can hold large numbers of larvae, especially where not stocked with fish. A further interesting habitat is the heathland bogs and pools in the west of the county, where larvae have been seen.

This is a common and widespread species in southern England and Wales, more local in the Midlands and rare in the north. Populations can be reinforced by immigrants, since it is a known migrant. It is found commonly throughout Surrey in all suitable habitats, even occurring, and probably breeding, as far in to London as Deptford and Barnes. Early records for this species in Lucas (1900) are from Richmond Park, Thames Ditton, Esher, Oxshott, Claygate, Send, Longcross, Ockham Common, Bookham, Ranmore Common and Horsley. One on 28th April from "Surrey" is the earliest date recorded, but alas without site or year. Longfield (1949) only stated that it was well distributed over all our area.

The flight period in Surrey ranges from May to early August but in years when the weather is suitable, it is found until early September. The earliest complete record is 4th May 1990 by J.Pontin at Danewell Gutter, Horsell Common, the latest 8th September 1991 by D.&J.Dell at Thursley Common.

Orthetrum cancellatum (Linnaeus, 1758)   PLATE 14   Black-tailed Skimmer

National status: local
Total records: 607
Number of tetrads: 117
Breeding status in Surrey:
  confirmed, widespread

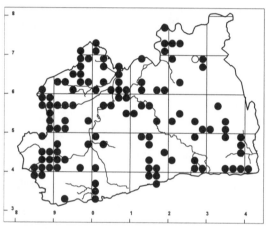

The mature male Black-tailed Skimmer has a powder-blue abdomen with a black tip and clear wings, but the abdomen of the female and immature male is brownish-orange with paired black curved markings resembling a 'ladder'. Males patrol territories by skimming very low over the water, often returning to a favoured perch or spot on the bare ground to bask in the sun. They can be aggressive towards other dragonflies of the same or different species, and are fairly territorial. Females often hide in nearby vegetation, but when ovipositing, which they do alone and directly into water, the males are often observed in attendance close by.

This species has a preference for shallow ponds, lakes, gravel-pits, bogs and canals, the acidity of which does not appear to be a factor, but the presence of bare mud, earth or sand with little vegetation is important for a successful breeding regime. It is one of the first colonisers of newly-created waters.

Nationally the Black-tailed Skimmer occurs in Great Britain only below a line from the Wash to the Dee, and is most commonly found in the Home Counties. In Surrey it is a common and widespread species which appears to be on the increase, due in no small way to the spread of gravel-pits and other excavations since the war. Lucas (1900) only knew this species from five localities: Ockham Common, a brick field at Merton, New Malden, near Byfleet and Chobham Common, while Longfield (1949) gave further sites such as Beddington, Esher, Epsom and Richmond. In the same publication Longfield also quotes a record from Leach in 1815 as "common on the Croydon Canal", a locality that unfortunately no longer exists.

The flight period in Surrey extends from the begining of June to early September, with the earliest record to date being 27th May 1990 by J.Silsby at Bay Pond and the latest 27th September 1985 by M.Thurner at Bolder Mere, Wisley.

Orthetrum coerulescens (Fabricius, 1798)   PLATE 14   Keeled Skimmer

National status: local
Total records: 246
Number of tetrads: 25
Breeding status in Surrey:
  confirmed, very local in west

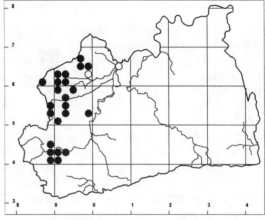

The mature male Keeled Skimmer also has a powder-blue abdomen with a thin black line down the centre (the keel). Females and immature males have orange-brown abdomens with a thin black central line. Both sexes have pale thoracic stripes and clear wings with a yellow pterostigma, and are slightly smaller than the Black-tailed Skimmer with which they can be confused. The female can attain the blue colouration of the male with age.

This is a species of acid bogs and marshes with sphagnum pools, wet flushes and streams. It flies low over the water along the edges, settling frequently on the ground or on adjacent vegetation. The species is not particularly territorial and up to 15 were observed feeding together at Thursley Bog in 1993.

Nationally it is a species that can be locally abundant on wet heathland in the south and south-west of England, and in Wales. It is scarcer further north, with a few localities in western Scotland. In Surrey it is restricted to the acid western heaths and bogs, being found locally but quite commonly on wet flushes issuing from bogs. It is usually common or even abundant at its main sites, such as Thursley, Pirbright, Bisley and Chobham Commons.

Lucas (1900) only knew this species from Weybridge and Bisley, while Harcourt-Bath (1890) gave "near Godalming", and Longfield (1949) reported Littleworth and Esher (occasional), but abundant on commons outside the London area.

The flight period in Surrey is from late May to early September with a peak in June and July. The earliest record to date is 22nd May 1990 by M.Thurner at Thursley Common and the latest 10th October 1995 by P.Follett, also at Thursley Common.

Sympetrum striolatum (Charpentier, 1840) PLATE 15 Common Darter

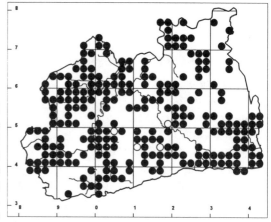

National status: common
Total records: 1404
Number of tetrads: 244
Breeding status in Surrey:
  confirmed, widespread and
  common

The male Common Darter is a dull red colour when mature, but the females and teneral males are a dull yellow-brown. The abdomen lacks the clubbed appearance of the Ruddy Darter, and the black legs have a yellow stripe in both sexes. This species can be very aggressive towards other dragonflies, of its own and different species. It settles often, on the ground, on low vegetation, or on any flat surface in sunshine. Immatures are often found away from water along woodland rides or thick hedgerows offering protection from wind and weather. Large aggregations may be partly due to an influx from the continent, because it is known to migrate, sometimes in association with other members of the genus.

Occurring on all forms of still water, canals and slow-flowing stretches of rivers, this is probably the most common and widespread dragonfly in Britain. In Surrey it is common and often abundant throughout the county including the extreme north-east, in the environs of London, where it frequently breeds in garden ponds.

Historical records of this species are not plentiful, possibly due to it being so well distributed and common. Lucas (1900) gave Esher, Ockham, Bookham and Chobham Commons, along with Richmond Park, near Thursley, Bisley, Chertsey and Woking, while Longfield (1949) only stated that "it is found at all still waters in the London area that are possible for a dragonfly to inhabit", again without any specific localities.

The flight period of the Common Darter in Surrey is from early July to the end of October, but it can occur in good numbers earlier or later if the weather is suitable, as in 1994 when the excepionally mild autumn produced records into December. The earliest record to date is 15th June 1993 by C.D.Lowmass at Hazel Bridge, Chiddingfold, the latest 4th December 1994 at Thursley by D.Tagg.

Sympetrum vulgatum (Linnaeus, 1758) Vagrant Darter

National status: vagrant/
  accidental
Total records: 2
Number of tetrads: 2
Breeding status in Surrey: not
  breeding, rare migrant

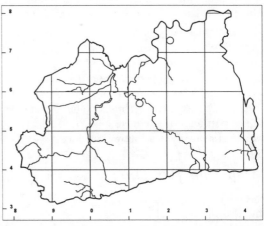

The Vagrant Darter is an extremely rare migrant which is very similar to the Common Darter in size, shape and colour, differing mainly in the black facial band which extends down the sides of the eyes, and the right-angled vulvar scale in the female; this scale is sloping in the Common Darter. These small differences may be one of the reasons why records for this species in Britain are few and far between. It would require the netting and examination of many Common Darters in order to distinguish a single Vagrant Darter.

Historically most of the records are from south-east England, with only two from Surrey during the last century. Lucas (1900) mentions that "Mr.Briggs has a male which he took at Bookham Common in 1891", and Longfield (1949) cites a male in Richmond Park in 1898. A small influx of this species occurred in August 1995 in Kent, but no specimens were recorded from Surrey. These were the first records in Britain since 1946.

Sympetrum fonscolombii (Selys, 1840) PLATE 15 Red-veined Darter

National status: migrant
Total records: 11
Number of tetrads: 6
Breeding status in Surrey:
  confirmed, only one old record

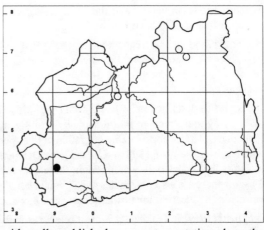

The male Red-veined Darter is a very beautiful insect, with its bright pinkish-scarlet, very slightly waisted abdomen and red-veined wings, often with a bluish tint. Females and immature males have the red of the abdomen and wings replaced by brownish-yellow. It is a species which prefers to fly over the open water of ponds and lakes with well-established emergent vegetation along the margins.

Red-veined Darters are rare migrants to the British Isles from southern Europe which have been known to breed. Unfortunately colonies do not appear to persist, the reasons for which are unknown, but may possibly be our lower winter temperatures.

This species has not been seen in Surrey since 1976, when J.Pontin saw a male at St.John's on the Basingstoke Canal. Prior to this record, the only reported occurrences in the county this century were in 1946 and on 13th August 1947, both at Frensham Great Pond where A.W.Richards caught two mature males on the latter date, in 1911 at Merton and in 1941 when several were taken on Wimbledon Common (Longfield, 1949). According to Lucas (1900), C.A.Briggs and his brother took 17 males on Ockham Common in June, 1892, all on one portion of Boldermere Lake. In the J.J.F.X.King collection at Glasgow there are two specimens labelled 'Surrey, 8th June 1892'.

Sympetrum flaveolum (Linnaeus, 1758)   PLATE 15   **Yellow-winged Darter**

National status: migrant
Total records: 54
Number of tetrads: 20
Breeding status in Surrey:
  confirmed, one old record

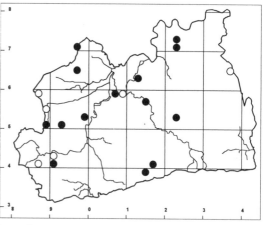

The Yellow-winged Darter is similar to our other red *Sympetrum* species, the male having a brownish-red thorax, an almost straight-sided red abdomen, and wings suffused with saffron at their bases for about a third of the wing area. The females are similar in shape, but with the abdomen brownish-yellow and the saffron suffusion also occurring at the nodes.

This noted migrant and frequent visitor to the British Isles occurs most years in the southwest on coastal pools, lakes and other suitable stretches of water. Occasionally it reaches the other southern counties of England, notably Surrey where it has occurred fairly frequently.

Lucas (1900) described pairs being seen on Shirley Heath near Croydon on 27th August 1871, flying in the tandem position and ovipositing, and goes on to say that "there is little doubt that in 1871 a considerable migration of this species took place". A further migration occurred in September 1898 and Lucas gave Ockham Common and Elstead as localities in Surrey, but males only were seen on these occasions. In the J.J.F.X.King collection at Glasgow there are also four males and a female labelled 'Surrey 1898'. Ockham Common was again the location for further records in 1899 and 1900 by W.J.Lucas.

Longfield (1949) stated that "it is most often met with on the Surrey ponds", and indeed it was recorded in Surrey throughout the years that followed, at irregular intervals up to 1975, as listed opposite.

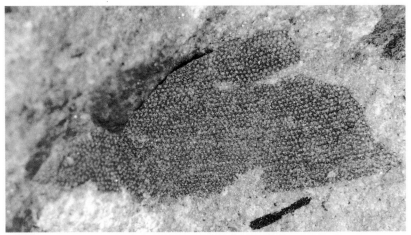

Figure 1. Eye of dragonfly, CH, after Jarzembowski (1984). Length 5mm.

Figure 2. *Cretacoenagrion alleni*, CH, wing after Jarzembowski (1990). Length 15mm.

Figure 3. *Mesocoenagrion martinae*, A, wing after Bechley *et al.* (1997 in press). Length 14mm.

PLATE 1

Figures 4a and 4b. *Cretarchistigma greenwoodi,* A, CH respectively, wing tips. Width 4mm.
Booth Museum BMB 018655, 018748.

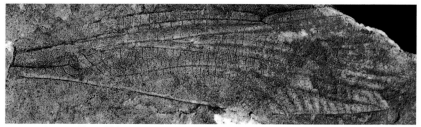

Figure 5. *Tarsophlebia* sp., CH, forewing after Jarzembowski (1987). Length 26mm.

Figure 6. Undescribed gomphid forewing, A. Length 22mm. BMB 018650.

PLATE 2

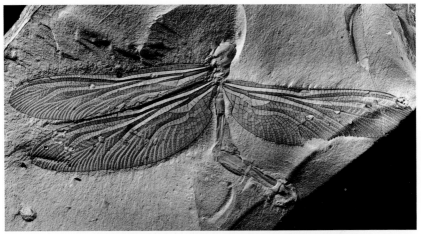

Figure 7. *Valdaeshna surreyensis,* A, male after Jarzembowski (1988b). Wingspan 92mm.

Figure 8. Unnamed hindwing base, CH, after Jarzembowski (1984). Width 9mm.

Figure 9. *Cretaneophya strevensi,* S, female hindwing base after Jarzembowski & Nel (1996). Width 6mm.

PLATE 3

Normandy Pond

Gracious Pond, Chobham

Hedgecourt Lake, Felbridge

Vann Lake, Ockley

Send Pond

PLATE 4

River Tillingbourne, Abinger Hammer

Basingstoke Canal, Ash Embankment

River Wey, Thundry Meadows, Elstead

Basingstoke Canal, St John's

Basingstoke Canal, Deepcut

PLATE 5

J E LYTLE

Thursley, Moat Pond

J E LYTLE

Thursley, East Bog

MIKE THURNER

Thursley Stream

PLATE 6

Calopteryx virgo Beautiful Demoiselle (m)   *Calopteryx virgo* Beautiful Demoiselle (f)

Calopteryx splendens Banded Demoiselle (m)   *Calopteryx splendens* Banded Demoiselle (f)

Lestes sponsa Emerald Damselfly (m)   *Lestes sponsa* Emerald Damselfly (f)

PLATE 7

MIKE THURNER

Lestes dryas   Scarce Emerald Damselfly (m)

DAVID ELEMENT

Platyenemis pennipes   White-legged Damselfly (m)

J P EARLY

Platyenemis pennipes   White-legged Damselfly (f)

DAVID ELEMENT

Pyrrhosoma nymphula   Large Red Damselfly

PETER BICKFORD

Erythromma najas   Red-eyed Damselfly (m)

PLATE 8

Coenagrion puella   Azure Damselfly (m)

Coenagrion puella   Azure Damselfly (f)

Coenagrion pulchellum Variable Damselfly (m)

Coenagrion pulchellum   Variable Damselfly (f)

Enallagma cyathigerum   Common Blue Damselfly (m)

PLATE 9

Ischnura pumilio Scarce Blue-tailed Damselfly (m)

Ischnura pumilio Scarce Blue-tailed Damselfly (f)

Ischnura elegans Blue-tailed Damselfly (f)

Ischnura elegans Blue-tailed Damselfly (f)

Ischnura elegans Blue-tailed Damselfly

Ceriagrion tenellum Small Red Damselfly (m)

Ceriagrion tenellum Small Red Damselfly (f)

PLATE 10

Aeshna juncea   Common Hawker (m)   *Aeshna juncea*   Common Hawker (f)

Aeshna mixta Migrant Hawker (m)   *Aeshna mixta*   Migrant Hawker (f)

Aeshna cyanea   Southern Hawker (m)   *Aeshna cyanea*   Migrant Hawker (f)

PLATE 11

Aeshna grandis   Brown Hawker (m)   *Aeshna grandis*   Brown Hawker (f)

Anax imperator   Emperor Dragonfly (m)

Brachytron pratense   Hairy Dragonfly (m)   *Brachytron pratense*   Hairy Dragonfly

PLATE 12

Gomphus vulgatissimus   Club-tailed Dragonfly (m)

Cordulegaster boltonii   Golden-ringed Dragonfly (f)

Cordulia aenea   Downy Emerald (m)

Somatochlora metallica   Brilliant Emerald (m)

Libellula quadrimaculata Four-spotted Chaser (m)

Libellula quadrimaculata Four-spotted Chaser (m)

PLATE 13

Libellula depressa   Broad-bodied Chaser (m)

Libellula depressa   Broad-bodied Chaser (f)

Orthetrum cancellatum   Black-tailed Skimmer (m)

Orthetrum cancellatum   Black-tailed Skimmer (f)

Orthetrum coerulescens   Keeled Skimmer (m)

Orthetrum coerulescens   Keeled Skimmer (f)

PLATE 14

Sympetrum striolatum   Common Darter

Sympetrum fonscolombii   Red-veined Darter (m)

Sympetrum flaveolum Yellow-winged Darter (m)

Sympetrum flaveolum   Yellow-winged Darter (f)

Sympetrum sanguineum   Ruddy Darter (m)

Sympetrum sanguineum   Ruddy Darter (f)

PLATE 15

Sympetrum danae   Black Darter (m)

Leucorrhinia dubia   White-faced Darter (m)

Leucorrhinia dubia   White-faced Darter (m)   *Leucorrhinia dubia*   White-faced Darter (f)

PLATE 16

These were the only records received for this species until 1995 when a large immigration occurred along the south and east coasts of the British Isles, with many subsequently finding their way to Surrey. Several of the sightings were of females ovipositing into dried-up mud or heavily vegetated areas. Future monitoring at the sites listed below may produce further records, possibly of larvae or native-bred adults.

1947 – **Frensham Pond**, 13.8, a male (A.W.Richards).

1954 – **Wisley Common**, 13.6, a teneral male (still limp), the only record to date of this species breeding in Surrey (Longfield, 1957).

1955 – **Wimbledon Common**, 6.9, 70 males, with 20 males on other Surrey ponds in the same year (Longfield, 1957).

Wisley Common, 9.9, a male taken by A.E.Gardner and used for illustration (Askew, 1988).

1964 – **Thursley Bog**, 13.6 (J.Sankey).

1970 – **Birchy Pond, Thursley Common**, about 50 males in September, with one still there on 7.10 (D.Baldock).

Pond Farm, Wisley Common, 15.9, four males (D.Baldock).

1975 – **Ockham Common**, 20.8, one male (D.Baldock).

Mytchett Lake, Basingstoke Canal, one male in August (C.O.Hammond).

1995 – **River Mole, Leatherhead**, 1.8, one male (J.Early).

Capel, 2-5.8, at least three males and one female (D.Fraser, P.Follett).

Moat Pond, Thursley, 6.8, several (J.D.Silsby).

Thursley Bog, 6.8, one male (D.Tagg); 5.9 (D.Dell).

Brook Pond, Whitmoor Common, 8.8, at least one male and two females (D.Dell).

Kiln Pond, Chobham Common, 8.8, one male (D.Dell).

Vann Lake, 9.8, one male and one ovipositing female (P.Follett).

Windsor Great Park, 9.8, three males (J.Ward-Smith).

Walton Heath, 10.8, two males and one female (D.Fraser).

Black Pond, Esher Common, 15.8, 3-5.9, 21.9, several on all dates (J.D.Silsby); 17.8, two males and one female (D.Tagg).

Wisley Common, 18.8, two males (D.Tagg).

Lakeside, Ash Vale, 1.9, five adults seen (C.R.Hall); 20.8, 23.8, 30.8, including ovipositing female on 20.8 (D.Dell).

Wimbledon Common, 3.9, 6.9, 21.9, 30.9, 1.10, 8.10, over 50 on 6.9 (D.Element); 21.9, one male (M.Bunce).

Normandy Pond, 22.8 (D.Dell).

Sympetrum sanguineum (Müller, 1764) PLATE 15 Ruddy Darter

National status: notable/Nb
Total records: 407
Number of tetrads: 58
Breeding status in Surrey:
  confirmed, increasing

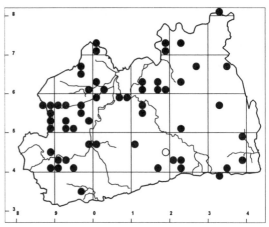

The Ruddy Darter is a small dragonfly with a fairly short blood-red abdomen with dark spots on segments eight and nine. A distinctive waist at segments three and four gives it a club shape. Females and teneral males are similar in shape but have yellowish-brown abdomens. Both sexes have clear wings and black legs. They have a flitting flight, settling often, and when ovipositing into water or mud, do so in tandem.

The preferred habitat is ponds and ditches with an abundance of reedmace, horsetail or bur-reed, among whose roots the larvae are often found. The males are territorial at breeding sites but the females often hide in the vegetation, making them difficult to find.

During the 1970s this species underwent a decline throughout its range in Britain, but has now recovered and certainly in Surrey is spreading to new sites. This may partly be due to migration, or to cyclic abundance in which there is a build-up of numbers in good summers, enabling it to expand its range to new localities. Indeed D.Baldock, in his survey from 1970 to 1980, knew of only one breeding site in Surrey, at a small pond on Ockham Common, with a further four localities with sight-only records, whereas today we have breeding records from twenty-two sites, and a further thirty-four where breeding has not been confirmed. Noted sites include Ockham Common, Basingstoke Canal, Newdigate Brickworks, Thursley Moat Pond, Thundry Meadows, Normandy Pond, Duncan Fraser Reserve at Capel, Runnymede, Bookham Common, Black Pond on Esher Common, and Brook Pond on Whitmoor Common.

Historically the Ruddy Darter had always been a scarce species in the county. Lucas (1900) only gave Ockham Common, but Longfield (1949) stated that "it is found yearly at all suitable ponds on the Surrey Commons and certainly breeds in many if not in most". Alas she did not give any details as to recorders or locations.

The flight period in Surrey extends from early July to early September, with the earliest record to date being 30th June 1993 at Bolder Mere by S.Price, and the latest 21st October 1985 at Felcourt by N.Donnithorne.

Sympetrum danae (Sulzer, 1776)   PLATE 16   Black Darter

National status: local in
England, common elsewhere
Total records: 408
Number of tetrads: 63
Breeding status in Surrey:
confirmed, local, mainly in west

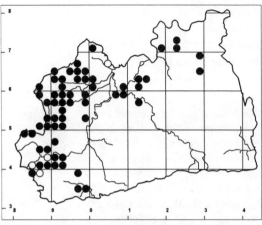

The male Black Darter is predominantly black with a club-
shaped abdomen and yellow
markings on the side of the thorax.
In the female and teneral male, the
abdomen is suffused with yellow
which becomes darker with age.
This is our smallest true dragonfly
and is not strongly territorial. It can often be seen feeding in large aggregations at favoured
sites, settling on the ground or on low vegetation, and is often very approachable.

Its habitats are acid bog-pools, flushes or ditches, often with sphagnum moss. The highest
numbers are usually found in sheltered spots. It is sometimes found far from breeding
sites, so any site which looks suitable should be closely watched. Although not usually
considered a migrant, this species was observed at Dungeness, Kent, during August 1995,
coming in off the sea in company with the Yellow-winged Darter and the Vagrant Darter.
It was also seen at Great Yarmouth, and later there were many reports of 'firsts' from
surrounding vice-counties. Nationally it is a common species in the north and west of
Britain, locally common on wet heaths in the south, but rare elsewhere. The Black Darter
is yet another west Surrey heathland speciality, being abundant in most years on all the
heaths with ponds, marshes and bogs, such as Thursley, Henleypark Lake, Chobham
Common, Royal Common, Esher Common and the Basingstoke Canal, where it flows
through heathland.

Lucas (1900) found the species emerging on 18th July 1897 at Esher Common, and used
the exuvia in his description. He also listed Ockham Common, near Elstead, Bookham
Common, Richmond Park, Bisley, Weybridge, Chobham Common and Chertsey. Longfield
(1949) gave Esher Common, Richmond Park, Bookham and Wimbledon Commons. Brooks
(1989) also gives breeding colonies on Wimbledon and Esher Commons, and other records
from Bookham and Mitcham Commons. There are post-1985 records for all the above-
mentioned localities, with the exception of Weybridge.

In Surrey the flight period is from July to late October, with the earliest record being 20th
June 1992 by J.Pontin at Danewell Gutter, Horsell Common, and the latest 3rd November
1989 at Thursley Common by M.Thurner.

Leucorrhinia dubia (van der Linden, 1825)   PLATE 16   **White-faced Darter**

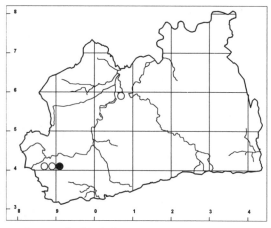

National status: notable/Na
Total records: 79
Number of tetrads: 4
Breeding status in Surrey:
confirmed, very local, at one
site only

The male White-faced Darter has a
black thorax with broad red stripes
and a black abdomen with red spots
on segments two, three, six and
seven. Females and teneral males
are similar, but with the red replaced
by yellow. Both sexes have the
prominent white face which gives
this species its name, and a dark brown base to the hindwings.

Females oviposit alone into wet peat, sphagnum or shallow water, and show a preference
for the shallow peaty pools with sphagnum margins on wet heathland in open situations.
The flight is low and fast, settling often. The species is territorial but not aggressive. When
disturbed, it flies quickly up and away across the heathland.

Its distribution in Britain is limited to the heaths and moorlands of Cheshire, Shropshire,
Cumbria and the Scottish Highlands, together with the Surrey heathland at Thursley
Common National Nature Reserve, the most southerly site in the country. In 1992 it was
also discovered in Suffolk, on the coast at Walberswick National Nature Reserve (Mendel,
1992).

In Surrey it was first found in June 1921 by Mr.Bateson, who took four males and two
females at Shining Glass Pond near Hindhead, of which two pairs were exhibited by
W.J.Lucas on 15th October 1924 at the Entomological Society of London. These specimens
were discovered by D.Baldock among the collections at Charterhouse School, together
with a letter from Lucas to Bateson, thanking him for the specimens. It was next seen at
Thursley by A.W.Richards in 1933. A second colony was discovered in 1954 at Pond
Farm, Wisley Common. Unfortunately this latter colony appears to have become extinct,
since the last specimen was seen in June 1977. A further four examples were seen in 1976
on the Flashes at Churt Common by D.Baldock, but with no indication of breeding, and it
was not seen here again. This species still occurs at Thursley, with records in all years up
to and including 1995, but at a low density. It appears to have favoured areas on Thursley
Bog, where larvae have been found in the past, but sadly not in the last three years to my
knowledge. Adults are still found, which perhaps indicates that this species is breeding at
a new site in the Thursley area.

The flight period in Surrey extends from early May to the end of August, with a peak in
the last week of May and the first week of June. The earliest date is 9th May 1971 at
Thursley by R.M.Fry, and the latest 2nd September 1971 at Thursley Bog by D.Winsland.

RARE VAGRANTS

Lestes dryas Kirby, 1890   PLATE 8   Scarce Emerald Damselfly

The only Surrey record of this species is of a specimen in the Leeds City Museum labelled 'Oxshott 1916' (per Skelton). It is however sufficiently similar to the Emerald Damselfly *(Lestes sponsa)* to have been overlooked in its habitat of overgrown ditches and dykes in water-meadows, but this is unlikely. The species occurs in Essex and North Kent, with old records from Sussex.

[*Sympetrum meridionale* (Selys, 1841)   Southern Darter

This extremely rare migrant has supposedly occurred once in Surrey, a female taken in 1847 and now in the Dale Collection in the Hope Department at Oxford. In Europe its distribution is essentially southern, extending from Spain to the Balkans, so its claim to British status is very tenuous when based on this, and other unconfirmed records.

Due to a suspicion of incorrect labelling, or even that no original label is present, the species account is enclosed in brackets, pending further investigation.]

APPENDIX 1 – Surrey sites with 17 or more species of Odonata

SITE	*C. virgo*	*C. splendens*	*L. sponsa*	*P. pennipes*	*P. nymphula*	*E. najas*	*C. puella*	*C. pulchellum*	*E. cyathigerum*	*I. elegans*	*C. tenellum*	*A. juncea*	*A. mixta*	*A. cyanea*	*A. grandis*	*A. imperator*	*B. pratense*	*C. boltonii*	*C. aenea*	*S. metallica*	*L. quadrimaculata*	*L. depressa*	*O. cancellatum*	*O. coerulescens*	*S. striolatum*	*S. vulgatum*	*S. fonscolombii*	*S. flaveolum*	*S. sanguineum*	*S. danae*	*L. dubia*	TOTAL
Ash Vale, Lakeside	-	+	+	+	+	+	+	-	+	+	-	+	+	-	+	+	+	-	+	-	+	+	+	-	+	-	-	+	+	-	-	20
Basingstoke Canal, Aldershot	-	+	+	-	+	+	+	-	+	+	-	-	+	+	+	+	+	-	+	+	+	-	+	-	+	-	-	-	+	+	-	19
Basingstoke Canal, Ash	-	+	+	-	+	+	+	+	+	+	-	+	+	+	+	+	+	-	+	+	+	+	+	-	+	-	-	-	+	+	-	22
Basingstoke Canal, Ash Common	-	+	+	-	+	+	+	-	+	+	-	+	+	+	+	+	+	-	+	+	+	+	+	-	+	-	-	-	+	-	-	20
Basingstoke Canal, Ash Vale	-	-	+	-	+	+	+	-	+	+	-	+	+	+	+	+	+	-	+	-	+	-	+	-	+	-	-	-	+	-	-	17
Basingstoke Canal, Brookwood	-	+	+	-	+	+	+	-	+	+	-	-	+	+	+	+	+	-	+	+	+	+	+	-	+	-	-	-	-	-	-	18
Basingstoke Canal, Cowshot Bridge	-	+	+	-	+	+	+	-	+	+	-	+	+	+	+	+	+	-	+	-	+	-	+	-	+	-	-	-	-	-	-	17
Basingstoke Canal, Curzon Bridge	-	+	+	-	+	+	+	-	+	+	-	+	+	+	+	+	+	-	+	+	+	+	+	-	+	-	-	-	+	-	-	20
Basingstoke Canal, Deepcut	-	+	+	-	+	+	+	-	+	+	-	-	+	+	+	+	+	-	+	+	+	-	+	-	+	-	-	-	+	-	-	18
Basingstoke Canal, Frimley Park Lake	+	+	+	-	+	+	+	-	+	+	-	-	+	+	+	+	+	-	+	+	+	-	+	-	+	-	-	-	+	-	-	19
Basingstoke Canal, Great Bottom Flash	-	+	+	-	+	+	+	-	+	+	-	-	+	+	+	+	+	-	+	+	+	-	+	-	+	-	-	-	+	-	-	18
Basingstoke Canal, Lock Ladder	+	+	+	-	+	+	+	-	+	+	-	+	+	+	+	+	+	-	+	+	+	+	+	-	+	-	-	-	+	-	-	21
Basingstoke Canal, Mytchett	+	-	+	-	+	+	+	-	+	+	-	-	+	+	+	+	+	-	+	-	+	-	+	-	+	-	-	-	+	-	-	17
Basingstoke Canal, Mytchett Flash	+	+	+	-	+	+	+	-	+	+	-	+	+	+	+	+	+	-	+	+	+	+	+	-	+	-	-	-	+	-	-	21
Basingstoke Canal, Pirbright	-	+	+	-	+	+	+	-	+	+	-	+	+	+	+	+	+	-	+	+	+	-	+	-	+	-	-	-	+	-	-	19
Basingstoke Canal, Potter's Pool	-	+	+	-	+	+	+	-	+	+	-	-	+	+	+	+	+	-	+	-	+	-	+	-	+	-	-	-	+	-	-	17
Bolder Mere, Wisley	+	+	+	-	+	+	+	-	+	+	-	+	+	+	+	+	+	+	+	+	+	+	+	+	+	-	-	-	+	+	-	24
Chobham Common	+	-	+	-	+	+	+	-	+	+	+	+	+	+	+	+	+	+	+	-	+	+	+	+	+	-	-	-	+	+	-	23
Chobham Common, Langshot Bog	-	-	+	-	+	-	+	-	+	+	+	+	+	+	-	+	-	-	+	-	+	-	+	-	+	-	-	-	+	+	+	17
Chobham Common, Round Pond	-	+	+	-	+	+	+	-	+	+	+	+	+	+	+	+	+	-	+	-	+	+	+	-	+	-	-	+	+	+	-	22
Epsom Common, Stew Ponds	-	-	+	-	+	+	+	-	+	+	-	-	+	+	+	+	+	-	+	-	+	+	+	-	+	-	-	-	+	-	-	17

SITE	*L. dubia*	*S. danae*	*S. sanguineum*	*S. flaveolum*	*S. fonscolombii*	*S. vulgatum*	*S. striolatum*	*O. coerulescens*	*O. cancellatum*	*L. depressa*	*L. quadrimaculata*	*S. metallica*	*C. aenea*	*C. boltonii*	*B. pratense*	*A. imperator*	*A. grandis*	*A. cyanea*	*A. mixta*	*A. juncea*	*C. tenellum*	*I. elegans*	*E. cyathigerum*	*C. pulchellum*	*C. puella*	*E. najas*	*P. nymphula*	*P. pennipes*	*L. sponsa*	*C. splendens*	*C. virgo*	TOTAL
Esher Common	-	+	+	-	-	-	+	-	-	+	+	+	+	+	+	+	-	+	+	+	+	+	+	-	+	+	+	+	+	+	-	22
Esher Common, Black Pond	-	+	+	+	-	-	+	-	+	+	+	+	+	-	+	+	+	+	+	+	+	+	+	-	+	+	+	+	+	+	-	24
Farm Pond, Wisley	-	+	+	+	-	-	+	-	+	+	+	-	+	-	+	+	+	+	+	+	-	+	+	-	+	-	+	-	+	-	-	19
Frensham Little Pond	+	+	-	-	-	-	+	-	+	-	+	+	-	+	+	+	+	+	+	-	-	+	+	-	+	+	-	-	+	+	-	18
Great Bookham Common	-	+	+	-	-	+	+	-	+	+	+	+	+	+	-	+	+	+	+	-	-	+	+	-	+	-	+	+	+	+	+	22
Hedgecourt Lake, Felbridge	-	+	+	-	-	-	+	-	+	+	+	-	+	-	+	+	-	+	+	-	-	+	+	-	+	+	+	-	+	+	+	19
Henleypark Lake	-	+	+	+	-	-	+	+	+	+	+	+	+	-	+	+	+	+	+	+	-	+	+	-	+	+	+	-	+	+	-	23
Lightwater Country Park	-	+	-	-	-	-	+	-	+	+	+	-	-	-	-	+	-	+	+	+	+	+	+	-	+	-	+	-	+	+	+	17
Middle Pond, Esher	-	-	+	-	-	-	+	-	+	+	+	+	+	+	-	+	-	+	+	+	-	+	+	-	+	+	+	+	+	+	-	20
Mytchett Lake	-	+	+	-	-	-	+	-	+	+	+	+	+	-	-	+	+	+	+	-	-	+	+	-	+	+	+	+	+	+	-	20
Newdigate, Old Brick Works	-	+	+	-	-	-	+	-	+	+	+	-	+	-	-	+	-	+	+	+	-	+	+	-	+	+	+	+	+	+	+	20
Normandy Pond	-	+	+	+	-	-	+	+	+	+	+	-	+	-	-	+	+	+	+	+	-	+	+	-	+	+	+	+	+	+	-	22
Ockham and Wisley Commons	-	+	+	-	-	-	+	-	+	+	+	+	+	-	-	+	-	+	+	+	-	+	+	-	+	-	+	-	+	+	+	19
Richmond Park	-	+	-	-	-	-	+	-	+	+	+	-	+	+	+	+	-	+	+	-	-	+	+	-	+	+	+	-	+	+	-	18
Royal Common, Elstead	-	+	+	+	-	-	+	+	+	+	+	+	+	+	+	+	-	+	+	+	-	+	+	-	+	-	+	-	+	+	-	22
Runnymede, Langhams Pond	-	+	+	+	-	-	+	-	+	+	+	+	+	+	+	+	+	+	+	+	-	+	+	-	+	+	+	-	+	+	-	23
Thundry Meadows, Elstead	-	+	+	+	-	-	+	+	+	+	+	+	+	+	+	+	+	+	+	+	-	+	+	-	+	-	+	-	+	+	+	24
Thursley Bog	+	+	+	+	-	-	+	+	+	+	+	+	+	+	+	+	+	+	+	+	+	+	+	-	+	+	+	-	+	+	+	27
Thursley Common	-	+	+	+	+	-	+	+	+	+	+	+	+	+	+	+	+	+	+	+	+	+	+	-	+	+	+	+	+	+	+	28
Thursley, Moat Pond	+	+	+	-	-	-	+	+	+	+	+	+	+	+	+	+	+	+	+	+	+	+	+	-	+	+	+	+	+	+	+	27
Vann Lake, Ockley	-	-	-	-	-	-	+	-	+	+	+	+	+	+	+	+	+	+	+	-	-	+	+	-	+	+	+	-	+	-	+	19
Whitmoor Common, Brook Pond	-	+	+	+	-	-	+	+	+	+	+	+	+	-	+	+	+	+	+	+	+	+	+	-	+	-	+	-	+	+	-	23
Wimbledon Common	-	+	+	-	+	-	+	-	+	+	+	-	-	-	-	+	+	+	+	+	-	+	+	-	+	-	+	-	+	-	-	17

APPENDIX 2 – Code of practice

British Dragonfly Society code of practice on collecting dragonflies in the United Kingdom

Assumptions and background information

1. Dragonflies should not be killed unnecessarily. Identification can often be achieved by observation, photography and by collecting exuviae, especially in countries like the United Kingdom where much is known about the Odonata fauna already. It is also possible to capture dragonflies, examine them and then release them undamaged. They should be released where they were caught and as soon as possible.

2. Dragonflies should only be killed when a useful purpose is served thereby. For example, the conservation value of faunistic surveys, local lists, etc., depend on the reliability of accurate taxonomic identification. Where doubt exists, an identifiable photograph should be taken or an identifiable drawing made, but when this is not possible, a voucher specimen should be collected.

3. The main concern is to prevent significant damage to populations, especially those of rare and vulnerable species.
   All the evidence suggests that collecting is almost always a negligible cause of damage to dragonfly populations, whereas serious and lasting damage can be caused by destruction or pollution of habitats. Nevertheless it is highly desirable to reduce risks as far as possible and to promote a conservation ethic.
   If children are not allowed to collect at all, they are less likely to become interested in dragonflies and, hence, they will not become concerned about their conservation. A balance has to be struck between preventing risk and engendering interest and study.

The occasions when dragonflies can legitimately be collected

(a) Rare and vulnerable species, and isolated populations of common species
   i) Collecting voucher specimens when exuviae are not available.
   ii) Collecting specimens as a necessary part of a study whose objective is to conserve the population or species concerned.
   iii) Collecting specimens as a necessary part of an educational display, whose aim is to promote the conservation of the species concerned.

(b) Common species
   i) Collecting specimens for reference in personal and institutional collections.
   ii) Collecting specimens for serious scientific research, e.g. anatomical, physiological, ecological or ethnological studies.
   iii) Collecting specimens for teaching purposes.
   iv) Collecting specimens for display, for educational and/or conservation purposes.

Points to be observed when collecting

The following have been adapted from the Code for Insect Collecting issued by the Joint Committee for the Conservation of British Insects. Bulletin of the Amateur Entomologists' Society, 31:99-101. (1972).

1 No more specimens than are strictly necessary for any purpose should be killed.

2 Readily identified species should not be killed if the object is to "look them over" for aberrations or for other purposes; if possible, insects should be examined while alive and then released where they were captured.

3 The same species should not be taken in numbers year after year from the same locality.

4 Specimens for exchange or disposal to other collectors should be taken sparingly or not at all.

5 Permission should always be sought from the landowner or occupier when collecting (or studying) on private land.

6 Conditions laid down by the grantor of permission to collect should always be complied with.

7 When collections are made on nature reserves or sites known to conservationists, a list of species collected (or observed) should be supplied to those responsible for managing the site.

8 The environment should be damaged as little as possible. Remember the needs of other organisms and the interests of other naturalists; be careful of vegetation, nesting birds and, particularly, rare species.

9 Waterweed and moss which has been worked for larvae should not be left on the bank but should be replaced in the water.

10 Discretion should be exercised when passing on, or making public, the location of rare and vulnerable species.

Collecting dragonflies and the law

The Norfolk Hawker (*Anaciaeschna isosceles* (Müller, 1767)) is currently the only species totally protected under the Wildlife and Countryside Act, 1981.

APPENDIX 3 - Addresses and Societies

Amateur Entomologists' Society
The Registrar, 22 Salisbury Road, Feltham, Middlesex TW13 0TH.

Biological Records Centre
Monks Wood Experimental Station, Abbots Ripton,
Huntingdon PE17 2LS.

British Dragonfly Society
Membership Office, 68 Outwoods Road, Loughborough,
Leicestershire LE11 3LY.

British Entomological and Natural History Society
Dinton Pastures Country Park, Davis Street, Hurst, Reading,
Berkshire RG10 0TH.

English Nature
Nature Conservancy Council for England, Northminster House,
Peterborough PE1 1UA.

Environment Agency
Kings Meadow House, Kings Meadow Road, Reading,
Berkshire RG1 8DQ.

Surrey Wildlife Trust
School Lane, Pirbright, Woking, Surrey GU24 0JN.

Odonata Recording Scheme:

South-East England Regional Recorder
Mrs.N.I.Welstead, 3 Kelvin Close, Hythe, Southampton, SO4 5LW.

Surrey Odonata Recorder
Mr.P.C.Follett, 105 Rickwood Park, Beare Green, Dorking,
Surrey RH5 4PR.

DMAP enquiries to:
Dr.Alan Morton, Blackthorn Cottage, Chawridge Lane, Winkfield,
Windsor, Berkshire SL4 4QR.

Fossil enquiries to:
Dr.E.A.Jarzembowski, Maidstone Museum and Art Gallery,
St Faith's Street, Maidstone, Kent ME14 1LH.

APPENDIX 4 - References

Anon., 1988.
Dig a Pond for Dragonflies.

Askew, R.R., 1988.
The Dragonflies of Europe. Harley Books,Colchester.

Bath, W.Harcourt, 1890.
An illustrated handbook of British dragonflies. Birmingham:
Naturalists' Publishing Co.

**Bechly, G., Martínez-Delclòs, X., Jarzembowski, E. A., Nel, A.,
Escuillé, F. & Coram, R., 1997 in press.**
The Mesozoic non-calopterygoid Zygoptera: *Cretaceous
Research.*

Bioscan, 1992.
*Summary of Basingstoke Canal Dragonfly Records
1968-1992. Report No.OX/0291/B.* Bioscan (Oxford).

Bratton, J.H. & Langlois, D., 1984.
Notes on the dragonflies of Bookham Common. *The London
Naturalist* 63:133-136.

British Dragonfly Society, 1988.
*Code of practice on collecting dragonflies in the United
Kingdom.* (Leaflet.)

Brooks, S.J., 1994.
Records from the London Natural History Society.

Brooks, S.J., 1989.
Odonata of London, current status.
The London Naturalist 68:109-131, 1989.

Campion, F.W. & Campion, H., 1912.
Notes on the Dragonfly season of 1911.
Entomologist 45:173-174.

Cham, S.A., 1986.
A cautionary note on the use of the discoidal cell (or triangle)
in the identification of *Somatochlora metallica* (van der
Linden) and *Cordulia aenea* (L.). *Journal of the British
Dragonfly Society*, Vol.2, No.1, 1986.

Cham, S.A., 1991.
The Scarce Blue-tailed Damselfly, *Ischnura pumilio*
(Charpentier): its habitat preferences in south-east England.
Journal of the British Dragonfly Society, 7:18-25.

Cham, Stephen, Brooks, Stephen J. & McGeeney, Andrew, 1995.
Distribution and habitat of the Downy Emerald Dragonfly *Cordulia aenea* (L.) (Odonata:Corduliidae) in Britain and Ireland. *Journal of the British Dragonfly Society*, Vol.11, No.2, October 1995.

Chatfield, June E., 1994.
Flora and fauna of Nonsuch Park, Ewell. *The London Naturalist*, No.73, Nov.1994, 77-142.

Chelmick, D.G., 1979.
Odonata. Dragonflies. Provisional. Atlas of the Insects of the British Isles. Part 7 (2nd edn). Abbots Ripton; Institute of Terrestrial Ecology.

Chelmick, D.G., Hammond, C.O., Moore, N.W. & Stubbs, A.E., 1980.
The conservation of dragonflies. Nature Conservancy Council.

Corbet, P.S., Longfield, C.E. & Moore, N.W., 1960.
Dragonflies. London: Collins (reprinted 1985).

Corbet, P.S., 1962.
A Biology of Dragonflies. Witherby Ltd, London. Reprinted by E.W.Classey, 1983.

Curtis, J., 1836.
British Entomology, Vol 13, no.616. London: published by the author.

d'Aguilar, J., Dommanget, J.-L. & Prechac, R., 1986.
A Field Guide to the Dragonflies of Britain,Europe and North Africa (English edition) 1986. Collins, London.

Dannreuther, T., 1942.
Migration records, 1942. *Entomologist* 75:55-63.

Day, Ruth, 1987.
Population Dynamics of Damselflies at Bookham Common. *The London Naturalist*, No.66, 1987.

Day, Ruth, 1988.
Survey of Bookham Common, 46th Year, 1987. *The London Naturalist*, No.67:156-159.

Day, Ruth, 1989.
Survey of Bookham Common for 1988; Odonata. *The London Naturalist*, No.68:141-143.

Day, Ruth, 1990.
Survey of Bookham Common, 1989. *The London Naturalist,*
No.69:128-130.

Day, Ruth, 1991.
Survey of Bookham Common,1990. *The London Naturalist,*
No.70:137-138.

Day, Ruth, 1992.
Survey of Bookham Common 1991. *The London Naturalist,*
No.71:162-166.

Day, Ruth, 1992.
Survey of Bookham Common, 1992. *The London Naturalist,*
No.72:109-111.

Day, Ruth, 1994.
Survey of Bookham Common, 1993. *The London Naturalist,*
No.73:172-173.

Doubleday, H.Arthur, (ed.), 1902.
The Victoria County History of Surrey, Vol.1, p78-79.

Dumont, H.J., 1973.
Mass migration in dragonflies, especially in *Libellula
quadrimaculata* L.: a review, a new ecological approach and a
new hypothesis. *Odonatologica* 2:1-20.

Evans, W.F., 1845.
British Libellulinae; or, dragonflies. Private publication
(printed by J.C.Bridgewater).

Fry, R.M., 1968.
Dragonflies (Odonata); list for Thursley SSSI and adjacent
land. *Surrey Naturalist 1968.*

Gambles, R.M., 1976.
A history of Odonatology in the British Isles.
Odonatologica 5:1-10.

Gardner, A.E., 1950.
The Life History of *Aeshna mixta* Latreille (Odonata).
Entomologist Gazette, Vol 1, pp128-138.

Gardner, A.E., 1951.
The Life History of *Sympetrum danae* (Sulzer)=*S.scoticum*
(Donovan) (Odonata). *Entomologist Gazette,* Vol 2,
pp109-127.

Gardner, A.E., 1953.
The Life History of *Leucorrhinia dubia* (van der Linden)
(Odonata) . *Entomologist Gazette*, Vol 4, pp45-65.

Gardner, A.E., 1953.
Further Notes on Exophytic Oviposition in Odonata.
Entomologist Monthly Magazine, Vol 89, pp98-99.

Gardner, A.E., 1954.
A key to the larvae of the British Odonata. *Entomologist's Gazette* **5**:157-71, 193-213.

Gibbons, B., 1986.
Dragonflies and damselflies of Britain and Northern Europe.
Newnes Country Life Books.

Hall, Chris, 1993.
The Dragonfly fauna of the Basingstoke Canal.

Hammond, C.O., 1983.
*The Dragonflies of Great Britain and Ireland. 2nd edition
(revised by R.Merritt).* Harley Books, Colchester. 116pp.

**Harland, W. B., Armstrong, R. L., Cox, A. V., Craig, L. E.,
Smith, A. G. & Smith, D. G. 1990.**
A geologic time scale. 263 pp. Cambridge University Press.

Heath, J., (ed.), 1978.
*Odonata. Dragonflies. Provisional Atlas of the Insects of the
British Isles. Part 7.* Abbots Ripton: Institute of Terrestrial
Ecology.

Hinnekint, B.O.N., 1973.
Mass migration in dragonflies, especially in *Libellula
quadrimaculata* L.: a review, a new ecological approach and a
new hypothesis. *Odonatologica* **2**:1-20.

Hold, A.J., 1994.
Records for VC17 Surrey, in a letter from I.T.E. South-east
England.

Jarzembowski, E. A., 1984.
Early Cretaceous insects from southern England. *Modern
Geology*, **9**: 71-93, pls 1-4.

Jarzembowski, E. A., 1987.
Early Cretaceous insects from southern England, 421 pp. PhD
thesis, University of Reading.

Jarzembowski, E.A., 1987.
The Surrey dragonfly. *Antenna* 11(1):12-13.

Jarzembowski, E. A., 1988a.
British dragonflies in the latter part of the age of dinosaurs.
Journal of the British Dragonfly Society, 4(1): 1-8.

Jarzembowski, E. A., 1988b.
A new aeshnid dragonfly from the Lower Cretaceous of
south-east England. *Palaeontology*, 31(3): 763-769.

Jarzembowski, E. A., 1990.
Early Cretaceous zygopteroids of southern England,
Odonatologica, 19(1): 27-37.

Jarzembowski, E. A., 1995.
Early Cretaceous insect faunas and palaeoenvironment.
Cretaceous Research, 16(6): 681-693.

Jarzembowski, E. A. & Nel, A., 1996.
New fossil dragonflies from the Early Cretaceous of SE
England and the phylogeny of the Superfamily Libelluloidea.
Cretaceous Research, 17(1): 67-85.

Joint Committee For The Conservation of British Insects, 1973.
British Odonata and Orthoptera: rare and endangered species.
Entomologist's Gazette 24:218.

Kett, S.M. & Kirk, R.S., 1994.
A survey of the aquatic macro-invertebrate communities of
Isle of Wight Pond and Western Hollow Pond, Bookham
Common. *The London Naturalist* 73:175-180.

Longfield, C.E., Cowley, J., Killington,F.J. & Kimmins, D.E., 1935.
The Generic names of the British Odonata with a check list of
the British species. Annex 2 to 3rd Rpt. Ctee. Generic
Nomencl. *Transactions of the Royal Entomological Society of
London* , pp.49-52.

Longfield, C.E., 1937.
The Dragonflies of the British Isles. Warne,London.

Longfield, C.E., 1949.
The Breeding Status of *Aeshna mixta* Lat. (Odonata) and
notes on the evidence of breeding in *Sympetrum flaveolum*
(L) and *S.fonscolombii* (Selys). *Journal of the Society for
British Entomology,* Vol.3, Pt.2 ,1949, pp.84-88. *Transactions
of the Society for British Entomology,* Vol.3, pt.2.

Longfield, C.E., 1949.
The Dragonflies of the London Area.
The London Naturalist **28**:90-98.

Longfield, C.E., 1949.
The Dragonflies of the British Isles. 2nd(enlarged) edition.
Frederick Warne, London.

Longfield, C.E., 1957.
Notes on the British Odonata (Dragonflies) for 1954 and 1955.
Entomologist **90**:44-49.

Lucas, W.J., 1899.
Dragonflies in 1898. *Entomologist* **32**:63.

Lucas, W.J., 1900.
British Dragonflies (Odonata). London: Upcott Gill.

Lucas, W.J., 1900.
The Dragonfly Season of 1899. *Entomologist* **33**:137-143.

Lucas, W.J., 1901.
Odonata in 1900. *Entomologist* **34**:65-69.

Lucas, W.J., 1902.
Dragonflies in 1901. *Entomologist* **35**:33-38.

Lucas, W.J., (Odonata ed.), 1902.
The Victoria County History of Surrey, Vol 1, p78-79.

Lucas, W.J., 1908.
Notes on the British dragonflies of the 'Dale Collection'.
Entomologist's Monthly Magazine **44**:198-203.

Lucas, W.J., 1930.
*The aquatic (naiad) stage of the British Dragonflies
(Paraneuroptera).* London:Ray Society.

McGeeney, Andrew, 1986.
A complete guide to British Dragonflies.

McLachlan, R., 1884.
The British dragonflies annotated. *Entomologist's Monthly
Magazine* **20**:251-256.

Mendel. W., 1992.
The Dragonflies of Suffolk. Ipswich: Suffolk Naturalists'
Society.

Merritt, R., Moore, N.W. & Eversham, 1996.
Atlas of the dragonflies of Britain and Ireland. Institute of
Terrestrial Ecology, Monks Wood.

Miller, P., 1991.
Dragonfly Survey of the Basingstoke Canal.
Report No.OX/0291/A. Report to Bioscan.

Miller, P.L., 1987.
Dragonflies.Naturalists Handbooks 7. Cambridge University
Press, Cambridge.

Moore, N.W., 1976.
The conservation of Odonata in Great Britain.
Odonatologica **5**:37-44.

Mundell, A.R.G., Shaw, E.J. & Dimmock, D.P., 1980.
MoD Wildlife Survey – Farnborough and Aldershot.
R.A.E. Conservation Group (Farnborough).

Mundell, A.R.G., 1991.
*Summary of Basingstoke Canal Dragonfly Records, Pondtail
to Aldershot.*

Mundell, A.R.G., 1992.
Basingstoke Canal Dragonfly Records. (Revised tables only.)

Mundell, A.R.G., 1992.
Summary of Basingstoke Canal Dragonfly Records.

Mundell, A.R.G., 1992.
Dragonflies of the Basingstoke Canal. Typescript of address
to the British Dragonfly Society Annual Conference, Oxford.

Nel, A. & Jarzembowski, E. A., 1996.
Description and revision of some dragonflies
('Anisozygoptera') from the Lower Cretaceous of England.
Cretaceous Research, **17**(1): 87-96.

Nel, A. & Jarzembowski, E. A.   Under review.
New Protomyrmeleontidae from the Lower Cretaceous of
southern England (Insecta, Odonata, Archizygoptera).
Cretaceous Research.

O'Farrell, A.F., 1950.
The J.J.F.X.King collection of British Odonata.
Entomologist **83**:14-18.

Paine, Alan (compiler), 1993.
Notes and observations: Odonata as prey. *Journal of the British Dragonfly Society*, Vol.9, No.1, p20, April 1993.

Paine, Alan (compiler), 1993.
Notes and observations: Behaviour. *Journal of the British Dragonfly Society*, Vol.9, No.1, p19, April 1993.

Parkinson, A., 1993.
Brachytron pratense in the Blackwater Valley. Report to the Blackwater Valley Management Service.

Payne, R.M., 1944.
Notes on the Distribution of Dragonflies on Bookham Common. *The London Naturalist*, 1944, No.24, pp23-31.

Pinniger, E.B., 1935.
Notes on dragonflies, 1934. *London Naturalist*, 1935, pp71-72.

Prendergast, N.H.D., 1988.
The distribution and abundance of *Calopteryx splendens* (Harris), *C.virgo* (L) and *Platycnemis pennipes* (Pallas) on the Wey river system (Hampshire and Surrey). *Journal of the British Dragonfly Society*, Vol.4, No.2, November 1988.

Pygott, J. & Eaton, J., 1993.
Basingstoke Canal SSSI Management Plan (Third Draft).

Reed, W., 1956.
Records of dragonflies supplied to J.Sankey.

Reynolds, F.L., 1972.
1971 Report Thursley Reserve and SSSI, Odonata. Surrey Wildlife Trust.

Richards, A.W., 1940.
Odonata of North-East Hampshire and North-West Surrey. *Journal of the Society for British Entomology* 2:61-63.

Richards, A.W., 1941.
Odonata of North East Hampshire and North-West Surrey. *Journal of the Society for British Entomology* 2:117-119.

Sage, M., 1956.
Records of dragonflies supplied to J.Sankey.

Sankey, J., 1952.
Surrey Biological Records Centre card index.

Savan, B., 1877.
The Status and Distribution of Dragonflies on the Tertiaries.
N.C.C.South Region (Newbury).

Stephens, J.F., 1836.
Illustrations of British entomology. Mandibulata. Vol.6.
London: Baldwin and Cradock.

Tillyard, R.J., 1917.
The Biology of Dragonflies.

Vick, G., 1987.
Key to larvae. In: **Miller, P.L., 1987.** *Dragonflies.* Cambridge:
Cambridge University Press.

Wycherley, J.T.M., 1992.
Holmwood Common pond survey for National Trust.

APPENDIX 5 - Gazetteer of sites

Albury: Belmount Copse	TQ0447	TQ04N
Ansteadbrook (golf course)	SU9232	SU93G
Ash Vale: Lakeside	SU8851	SU85V
Ashtead Common	TQ1659	TQ15U
Ashtead Common: Flag Pond	TQ1760	TQ16Q
Ashtead Park	TQ1958	TQ15Z
Barossa Common, Camberley	SU8661	SU86Q
Basingstoke Canal: A324 Pirbright	SU9456	SU95N
Basingstoke Canal: Ash	SU8851	SU85V
Basingstoke Canal: Ash Common	SU8952	SU85W
Basingstoke Canal: Ash Vale	SU8953	SU85W
Basingstoke Canal: Brookwood	SU9557	SU95N
Basingstoke Canal: Cowshot Bridge	SU9356	SU95I
Basingstoke Canal: Curzon Bridge	SU9156	SU95D
Basingstoke Canal: Deepcut	SU9056	SU95D
Basingstoke Canal: Frimley Park Lake	SU8956	SU85Y
Basingstoke Canal: Goldsworth	SU9858	SU95Z
Basingstoke Canal: Great Bottom Flash	SU8953	SU85W
Basingstoke Canal: Lock Ladder	SU9256	SU95I
Basingstoke Canal: Mytchett	SU8954	SU85X
Basingstoke Canal: Mytchett Flash	SU8953	SU85W
Basingstoke Canal: Mytchett Lake	SU8954	SU85X
Basingstoke Canal: nr Blackhorse Road Bridge	SU9657	SU95T
Basingstoke Canal: West Byfleet	TQ0461	TQ06K
Basingstoke Canal: Pirbright Camp	SU9256	SU95I
Basingstoke Canal: Potter's Pool	SU8955	SU85X
Basingstoke Canal: Sheerwater	TQ0260	TQ06F
Basingstoke Canal: St John's Lye	SU9757	SU95T
Basingstoke Canal: Wharfenden Lake	SU8956	SU85Y
Basingstoke Canal: Woking	TQ0159	SU05E
Basingstoke Canal: Woking/Horsell	SU9958	SU95Z
Bay Pond, Godstone	TQ3551	TQ35K
Beare Green Lake	TQ1742	TQ14R
Beare Green Village Pond	TQ1743	TQ14R
Bearehurst Lakes	TQ1642	TQ14R
Beaver Farm Ponds, Felbridge	TQ3640	TQ34Q
Beddington Sewage Farm	TQ2966	TQ26Y

Blindley Heath: Red Barn Pond	TQ3645	TQ34S
Bolder Mere, Wisley	TQ0758	TQ05U
Bonds Lane Pond, Holmwood	TQ1646	TQ14T
Bookham Common	TQ1256	TQ15I
Botany Bay, Tugley Wood	SU9734	SU93S
Boundary Wood, Charleshill	SU8944	SU84X
Brentmoor Heath: Crater Pond and Burntstubb Pond	SU9360	SU96F
Brickfields Lake, Littleton	SU9846	SU94Y
Britten's Pond, Jacobswell	SU9953	SU95W
Brockham Hill Wood	TQ1950	TQ15V
Brookwick Copse, Leith Hill	TQ1345	TQ14H
Broome Hall Lake	TQ1542	TQ14L
Broomhall Heath, Wentworth	SU9666	SU96T
Buckland Village Pond	TQ2250	TQ25F
Bulhausen Farm Pond, Bisley Common	SU9459	SU95P
Bummoor Copse, Compton	SU9647	SU94T
Bury Hill Lake, Westcott	TQ1548	TQ14P
Campsite Pool, Tilford	SU8742	SU84R
Capel Village Pond	TQ1740	TQ14Q
Chobham Common: Albury Bottom	SU9864	SU96X
Chobham Common: Burnt Hill	SU9666	SU96T
Chobham Common: Fish Pool	SU9963	SU96W
Chobham Common: Four Horseshoes Pond	SU9762	SU96R
Chobham Common: Gracious Pond	SU9864	SU96X
Chobham Common: Langshot Bog	SU9763	SU96R
Chobham Common: Longcross	SU9765	SU96S
Chobham Common: Round Pond	SU9664	SU96S
Chobham Common: Valley End	SU9564	SU96M
Church Pond, North Holmwood	TQ1647	TQ14T
Coldharbour Pond	TQ1443	TQ14L
Cook's Pond, Dormans Park	TQ3940	TQ34V
Coulsdon Common	TQ3257	TQ35I
Duncan Fraser Reserve, Capel	TQ1740	TQ14Q
Durkins Pond, East Grinstead	TQ3939	TQ33Z

Earlswood Lakes	TQ2748	TQ24U
Eden Brook, Lingfield	TQ3943	TQ34W
Eden Brook, Felbridge	TQ3742	TQ34R
Edolphs Copse, Charlwood	TQ2342	TQ24G
Effingham Forest	TQ0955	TQ05X
Epsom Common: Stew Ponds	TQ1860	TQ16V
Esher Common	TQ1362	TQ16G
Esher Common: Black Pond	TQ1262	TQ16G
Ewhurst Road Pond, Peaslake	TQ0943	TQ04W
Ewhurst Village Pond	TQ0939	TQ03Z
Fetcham Mill Pond	TQ1556	TQ15N
Fire Pond, Wotton	TQ1346	TQ14I
Forest Green Pond	TQ1241	TQ14F
Forked Pond, Thursley	SU9141	SU94A
Fourwents Pond, Holmwood	TQ1845	TQ14X
Frensham Great Pond	SU8440	SU84K
Frensham Little Pond	SU8641	SU84Q
Friday Street Pond	TQ1245	TQ14H
Gatton Park, near Redhill	TQ2852	TQ25W
Glovers Wood, Charlwood	TQ2340	TQ24F
Godstone Reservoirs	TQ3451	TQ35K
Gomshall Marsh	TQ0847	TQ04Y
Gowan Lodge Pond, Holmwood Common	TQ1746	TQ14T
Halls Spring, North Holmwood	TQ1647	TQ14T
Hambledon Village Pond	SU9638	SU93U
Hammer Pond, Thursley	SU9140	SU94A
Haslemere Museum Ponds	SU9033	SU93B
Haxted Mill	TQ4145	TQ44C
Headley Heath	TQ2053	TQ25B
Hedgecourt Lake, Felbridge	TQ3540	TQ34K
Henfold Lakes, Newdigate	TQ1843	TQ14W
Henleypark Lake	SU9353	SU95G
Herons Reach, Lower Farm, Effingham	TQ1155	TQ15C
Hersham Sewage Farm	TQ1265	TQ16H
Hillhouse Farm Wood	TQ1842	TQ14W
Holmbury St Mary Pond	TQ1144	TQ14C

Holmwood Common	TQ1745	TQ14S
Horsell Common	TQ0060	TQ06A
Imbhams Farm Lake, Grayswood	SU9233	SU93G
Joyce's Meadow, Charleshill	SU8944	SU84X
Juniper Hall Field Centre, Mickleham	TQ1752	TQ15R
Kew Gardens	TQ1876	TQ17Y
Ladycross Lake, Dormansland	TQ4141	TQ44A
Leith Hill	TQ1443	TQ14L
Leith Hill Wood	TQ1342	TQ14G
Lightwater Country Park	SU9162	SU96B
Lightwater: Folly Bog	SU9261	SU96F
Lingfield Park	TQ3943	TQ34W
Little Blackmole Pond, Ottershaw	TQ0162	TQ06B
Littleton (area)	SU9847	SU94Y
Loseley Lake and Moat	SU9747	SU94T
Mercers Park, South Merstham	TQ3052	TQ35B
Mere Pond, Banstead Heath	TQ2255	TQ25H
Mitcham Common	TQ2868	TQ26Z
Mytchett Lake	SU8954	SU85X
Newdigate: Old Brick Works	TQ2042	TQ24B
Nonsuch Park, Cheam	TQ2263	TQ26G
Normandy Pond	SU9251	SU95F
North River, near Ockley	TQ1537	TQ13N
Nower Wood, Headley	TQ1954	TQ15X
Ockham and Wisley Commons	TQ0759	TQ05U
Ockley Common	SU9141	SU94A
Ockley Court Lake	TQ1540	TQ14K
Ockley Station Ponds	TQ1640	TQ14Q
Old Brickworks Pond, Ockley Road	TQ1642	TQ14R
Ottershaw Chase: Tanglewood Cottage	TQ0163	TQ06B
Oxshott Heath	TQ1360	TQ16F
Pikes Pool, Lower Farm, Effingham	TQ1155	TQ15C
Pond Farm, Wisley	TQ0759	TQ05U
Postford Pond, Albury Mill	TQ0347	TQ04I

Pucks Pool, Wisley (Sanguineum Pond)	TQ0858	TQ05Z
Puttenham Common: General's Pond	SU9146	SU94D
Puttenham Common: The Tarn	SU9145	SU94C
Puttenham Common: Warren Pond	SU9046	SU94D
Redhill Common	TQ2749	TQ24U
Redlands Bank Memorial Pond, Holmwood Common	TQ1645	TQ14S
Richmond Park	TQ1971	TQ17V
River Mole: A246 Bridge, Leatherhead	TQ1655	TQ15S
River Mole: Box Hill Stepping Stones	TQ1751	TQ15Q
River Mole: Boxhill Bridge	TQ1850	TQ15V
River Mole: Brockham	TQ1949	TQ14Z
River Mole: Flanchford Bridge	TQ2347	TQ24I
River Mole: Gatwick	TQ2641	TQ24Q
River Mole: Mickleham	TQ1753	TQ15R
River Mole: Rice Bridge	TQ2248	TQ24J
River Mole: Sidlow Bridge	TQ2547	TQ24N
River Mole: Stoke d'Abernon	TQ1358	TQ15J
River Wandle: Spencer Road Wetlands	TQ2766	TQ26T
River Wey Meadows, Send	SU8943	SU84W
River Wey Navigation: Artington	SU9947	SU94Y
River Wey Navigation: Bower's Lock	TQ0152	TQ05B
River Wey Navigation: Broadford Bridge	SU9946	SU94Y
River Wey Navigation: Broadmead Cut	TQ0256	TQ05I
River Wey Navigation: Cartbridge	TQ0156	TQ05D
River Wey Navigation: New Haw	TQ0562	TQ06L
River Wey Navigation: Newark Bridge	TQ0357	TQ05I
River Wey Navigation: Newark Lock	TQ0457	TQ05N
River Wey Navigation: Papercourt Lock	TQ0356	TQ05I
River Wey Navigation: Stoke Lock	TQ0051	TQ05A
River Wey Navigation: Walsham Meadow	TQ0457	TQ05N
River Wey Navigation: Walsham Towpath	TQ0558	TQ05P
River Wey: Eashing	SU9443	SU94L
River Wey: Elstead Bridge	SU9043	SU94B
River Wey: Farnham	SU8547	SU84N
River Wey: Send Grove	TQ0154	TQ05C
River Wey: Whipley Manor	TQ0341	TQ04F

River Wey: Wisley	TQ0659	TQ05U
River Wey: Wonersh Bridge	TQ0145	TQ04C
Riverside Park, Horley	TQ2841	TQ24V
Royal Common, Elstead	SU9242	SU94G
Royal Common: Guinea Pond	SU9142	SU94B
Runnymede Meadows	TQ0072	TQ07B
Runnymede: Langhams Pond	TQ0071	TQ07A
Selhurst Common	TQ0141	TQ04A
Send Pond	TQ0355	TQ05H
Shalford Marsh	SU9947	SU94Y
Shalford Pond	TQ0046	TQ04D
Sherbourne Pond, near Albury	TQ0648	TQ04U
Sidney Wood, near Alfold	TQ0133	TQ03B
Silent Pool, Shere	TQ0648	TQ04U
Stockbridge Pond, Tilford	SU8742	SU84R
The Flashes, Churt Common	SU8640	SU84Q
The Hatches, Frimley Green	SU8757	SU85T
Thundry Meadows, Elstead	SU8944	SU84X
Thursley Bog	SU9041	SU94A
Thursley Common	SU9040	SU94A
Thursley Stream	SU9041	SU94A
Thursley: Moat Pond	SU8941	SU84V
Thursley: Pudmore Pond	SU9041	SU94A
Tillingbourne Ponds, Wotton Estate	TQ1346	TQ14I
Tillingbourne: Albury	TQ0547	TQ04N
Tillingbourne: Gomshall Mill	TQ0847	TQ04Y
Tilling Springs Pond, Leith Hill	TQ1444	TQ14M
Tuesley Reservoir, Godalming	SU9642	SU94R
Tyting Farm Pond, near Chilworth	TQ0248	TQ04J
Vale Farm Ponds, Wotton	TQ1248	TQ14J
Vann Lake, Ockley	TQ1539	TQ13P
Virginia Water	SU9768	SU96U
Wallis Wood	TQ1238	TQ13J
Waterlands Pond, Holmwood Common	TQ1845	TQ14X
Waterloo Pond, Albury	TQ0448	TQ04P

Weare Street Pond, Ockley	TQ1639	TQ13U
Weavers Pond, Ockley	TQ1440	TQ14K
Westend Common, Pirbright Ranges	SU9260	SU96F
Wey & Arun Canal: Birtley	TQ0143	TQ04B
Wey & Arun Canal: Fast Bridge	TQ0436	TQ03N
Wey & Arun Canal: Tickford	TQ0235	TQ03H
Whitmoor Common	SU9853	SU95W
Wimbledon Common	TQ2371	TQ27F
Windsor Great Park: Cow Pond	SU9771	SU97Q
Wire Mill Lake, Felbridge	TQ3641	TQ34Q
Wisley Gardens RHS	TQ0658	TQ05U
Witley Common	SU9341	SU94F
Wormley Pond	SU9538	SU93P
Wotton House Pond	TQ1146	TQ14D
Wyke Common	SU9152	SU95B

APPENDIX 6 - Glossary

Anisoptera	The true dragonflies, with the fore and hind wings shaped differently.
Common/Nr	Nationally common, but scarce in the south-east (regionally notable).
Copulation	When the male sperm is transferred from the secondary genitalia to the female, in the wheel position.
Costa (costal)	The thickened vein at the leading edge of all four wings.
Emergence	The act of escaping, by the adult winged dragonfly, from its larval case.
Endophytic	Laying, of usually elongate eggs, into plant tissue.
Exophytic	Laying, of usually round eggs, externally onto plants or direct into mud or water.
Exuvia	The empty larval case, after emergence of winged adult.
Imago	The adult, winged dragonfly.
Instar	Each stage of larval growth.
Larva (or Nymph)	The second, aquatic stage in the dragonfly life cycle.
Metamorphosis	The bodily change from larva to adult.
Moult	The shedding of the larval skin to allow growth, which can occur up to 15 times.
Notable/Na	Nationally scarce, found in fewer than 30 of the 10km squares in Britain.
Notable/Nb	Nationally scarce, found in fewer than 100 of the 10km squares in Britain.
Odonata	Scientific name for dragonflies and damselflies.
Ovipositing	Act of laying eggs.
Primary genitalia	The sperm-producing organs, near the tip of the male's abdomen.
Pterostigma	A small mark adjacent to the costal edge of the wing, often dark in colour.

Secondary genitalia Male organs situated ventrally, on the second and part of the third abdominal segment.

Teneral Immature, as in a recently emerged dragonfly, prior to attaining its full adult coloration.

Thorax Part of the body between head and abdomen, to which the wings and legs are attached.

Tibia Second segment of the leg.

Venation The pattern of veins in the wings.

Wheel position Mating position, in which the male's claspers hold the female by the neck, while the female's genitalia are attached to the male's secondary genitalia near the base of the abdomen.

Zygoptera The damselflies, with fore and hind wings usually of the same shape.

INDEX

Figures in bold indicate plate numbers

INDEX

Figures in bold indicate plate numbers

steward of the Surrey Wild Life Trust
at the Bourne Society's AGM
Tithe Pit Shaw Rd, Warlsey Green
21.3.98
new £12